Building Blocks

Carole Gauthier
Gwenn Gauthier

In consultation with
Pierre Richard,
Cégep François-Xavier-Garneau

CEC

LES ÉDITIONS CEC INC.

8101, boul. Métropolitain Est, Anjou, Qc, Canada H1J 1J9
Téléphone: (514) 351-6010   Télécopieur: (514) 351-3534

Managing Director, ESL:
Leena Sandblom

Production Manager:
Lucie Plante-Audy

Project Editor:
Lori Schubert

Cover and page design:
Axis communication

Illustrations:
Michel Bisson

Acknowledgements:

The authors would like to express their
thanks to:

The participants of the focus group held in
the fall of 1997 in Quebec City, for their
helpful comments and observations.

Those who read the manuscript as it was
being developed, for their invaluable advice:

- Esther Chabot, ESL consultant from the
  Commission scolaire du Lac-Saint-Jean
- Réjean Garon, Secondary 5 teacher from
  l'École secondaire Mont-Sainte-Anne
  (Commision scolaire des Chutes-
  Montmorency)
- Nathalie McCarthy, Secondary 5 teacher
  from Centre Sésame (Commission scolaire
  du Goéland)
- Ada Perreault, Secondary 5 teacher from
  l'École secondaire Calixa-Lavallée (CECM)

Special thanks to Pierre Richard, ESL teacher
at the Cégep François-Xavier-Garneau, for his
work as principal consultant on the project,
and for his insightful comments and
suggestions.

Leena M. Sandblom, whose professionalism
and dedication made this project possible.

Lori Schubert, for her fastidious editing and
tireless fine-tuning of the manuscript.

Claude Bernard and his creative team, for
their fine graphic work and exceptional
design.

We would also like to thank Isabelle Gagnon,
Éric Couto, Bruno Dion and David Gagné for
their generous collaboration.

CONTENTS

Listening

Level I

L-1 Colours and You 2
L-2 Zac and Valerie 4
L-3 How to Study 6
L-4 How Well Do You Eat? 8

Level II

L-5 Woolly Slope-Keepers 10
L-6 A Different Kind of Job 12
L-7 The Dawning of Yawning 14
L-8 Using Computers 16

Level III

L-9 Is It True Love? 18
L-10 It's All in Your Nose 20
L-11 Parents Who Spy 22
L-12 UFO Encounters 24

Level IV

L-13 Buzz-Slap-Slap! 26
L-14 White-Water Rafting 28
L-15 It's All Right to Be Left 30
L-16 To Be or Not To Be Part of the Cool Crowd 32

Reading

Level I

R-1 That Very First Car 36
R-2 Your Life is in Your Hands 40
R-3 When Sylvia Dates 43
R-4 The King of Horror 47

Level II

R-5 Murphy's Law and School Life 50
R-6 Use Sense, Not Cents: How to Celebrate Your Prom Wisely 54
R-7 Guy Talk 58
R-8 Thrills, Chills and Hot Buttered Popcorn 61

Level III

R-9 Fishy Sea-Serpent Stories 64
R-10 Break-up Crisis 68
R-11 All Around Us 72
R-12 When an Ironman is a Woman 76

Level IV

R-13 Operation Noah 80
R-14 Cryopreservation: The Prospect of Immortality 84
R-15 Knitting with Steel 87
R-16 Stereotypes, or Judging a Book by its Cover 91

Production

P-1 The Simple Present   96

Writing an E-mail Message (W.P.) 100
Information Search (O.P.) 102

P-2 The Simple Past   104

Writing about a Personal Hero (W.P.) 107
When I Was Young (O.P.) 108

P-3 The Present Continuous   110

Writing a Children's Story (W.P.) 115
Telling Stories Based on Pictures (O.P.) 117

P-4 The Future   118

After High School (W.P.) 122
Going Back to the Future (O.P.) 124

P-5 Modals   125

Restricting Driver's Licenses to People Who are 18 or Older (W.P.) 128
What Makes a Good Friend? (O.P.) 130

P-6 The Present Perfect   131

Writing a Cover Letter for a Job Application (W.P.) 135
Job Interviews (O.P.) 136

P-7 The Possessive Forms   138

Stating Your Opinion (W.P.) 141
One Big, Happy Family (O.P.) 143

P-8 The Past Continuous   145

Writing about a Childhood Memory (W.P.) 148
Talking about Embarrassing Situations (O.P.) 150

Verbs   151

Irregular Verbs   153

Contents

LISTENING ACTIVITIES
STRATEGIES FOR LISTENING

Before listening

Predict what the text will say by...

Asking questions about the topic
Brainstorming on the topic of a text
Focusing on familiar words
Focusing on key words to understand a text
Guessing the meaning of unfamiliar words
Linking the title to the topic of a text
Thinking about what you already know about the topic
Thinking about what you want to know about the topic
Using the title and illustrations to get the general idea of a text

While listening

Monitor your comprehension by...

Asking yourself questions about the topic
Focusing on key words to understand a text
Focusing on key words to find specific information
Identifying the sequence of events
Identifying the type and purpose of a text
Listening for the general idea of a text
Listening for specific information
Organizing the information you learned about the topic
Thinking of the information you want to find
Using the context to guess the meaning of unfamiliar words
Verifying your answers
Verifying your predictions

After listening

Verify your comprehension by...

Answering the questions "Who?" "What?" "Where?" "When?" etc.
Expressing your opinion about what you heard
Identifying the sequence of events
Retelling the information in your own words
Thinking about what you learned about the topic
Using the information you learned from the text
Using what you learned to express your own ideas

1-1 COLOURS
AND YOU

People often associate different colours with different emotions or personality traits. For example, the colour red is often associated with anger or power.

Before listening

> *Thinking about the topic of a text*

1 What comes to mind when you think of the following colours? Associate a colour with each of the different personality traits.

> blue green red orange yellow brown black purple white pink

	MY IDEA	THE TEXT SAYS
1. Quiet, well-controlled		
2. Cheerful, optimistic		
3. Sociable, outgoing		
4. Serious		
5. Powerful, emotional, likes people		
6. Meticulous and clean, philosophical		
7. Warm, practical, creative		
8. Hardworking, responsible		

While listening

> *Verifying your ideas*

2 Listen to the recording and complete the chart. Did your ideas match the text?

3 Read the description of each person. Highlight the words that best describe his or her personality. Listen to the text again and decide which colour that person likes to wear.

1. Kathy has lots of friends. She simply loves to talk to others. She expresses herself easily and is a member of the drama club. She is working on her second play this year.

   Her colour is: _____

2. Francis is one of those people who seldom make noise. He rarely gets angry. He thinks anger is an illogical emotion. He prefers working out his problems to exploding.

   His colour is: _____

3. Sandra loves animals and plants. She is very innovative and likes to try new things. She always comes up with original solutions to her problems. She tends to look on the bright side of life.

   Her colour is: _____

4. Ted doesn't like change very much. However, when he does try something new, he keeps an open mind. It is sometimes difficult to know what he is feeling. Everything he does, he does well.

   His colour is: _____

5. Jenny is very devoted to her family and friends. She is often called on to baby-sit in the neighbourhood. She is quite reliable and takes her work seriously.

   Her colour is: _____

After listening

4 What colour best describes your personality? Explain your choice.

_____

_____

_____

_____

L1-2

ZAC
AND VALERIE

Family life can be a source of problems for many teenagers. When there's no one else to talk to, you can always turn to radio shows that have open lines especially for teens. Listeners can call the radio station and try to find solutions by sharing their own personal experiences.

Before listening

Thinking about what you already know about the topic

1 Zac and Valerie have problems related to their family lives. Based on your personal experience, make a few predictions about what the text might say.

_____

_____

_____

_____

While listening

Verifying your predictions

2 Listen to the tape and underline the predictions in number 1 that were right.

3 Read the list of solutions in the table below. Put a check mark to indicate whether they are intended for Zac or Valerie, or maybe even someone not on today's show.

Solutions	Zac	Valerie	Not on Today's Show
1. ...can worry that their children don't love them anymore. So reach out and let her know that you love her too.	☐	☐	☐
2. ...counselling can help them to mature emotionally and teach them how to handle themselves.	☐	☐	☐
3. ...how bad the situation is for you and ask them to confront their immature daughters.	☐	☐	☐
4. ...and she should listen to what they have to say.	☐	☐	☐
5. ...tell him to contact the authorities.	☐	☐	☐
6. ...trust is the key thing in a relationship, and the best thing for you to do is to dump him.	☐	☐	☐
7. ...be patient. You have to realize that she is making major adjustments in her life.	☐	☐	☐

After listening

Retelling the information in your own words

4 Use your own words to explain Zac's **or** Valerie's problem.

5 What advice can you give Zac **or** Valerie?

TO STUDY

Every student knows that you have to invest some time studying if you want to do well in your courses. The best way to spend your study time, however, is a matter of opinion.

Before listening

> *Brainstorming on the topic of a text*

1 Work with a classmate and discuss the ways you both study. Talk about where you like to study, the amount of time you study, and the different techniques you use.

What points do you have in common? What points are different?

SAME	DIFFERENT

While listening

> *Identifying the type and purpose of a text*

2 Listen to the recording and decide if the text...
a) gives information on the correct way to study.
b) gives opinions on how to study.
c) describes the relationship between studying and success.
d) gives opinions on the importance of studying.

How to Study

LISTENING

Focusing on key words

3 Look at the list below. Listen to the recording again. Indicate which of Sarah's and Fredrick's studying tips are different. List the words that helped you decide when the information was different.

STUDYING TIPS ON:	DIFFERENT	KEY WORDS
Place to study	☐	_____
Studying quietly	☐	_____
Study time	☐	_____
Writing notes	☐	_____
Reviewing notes	☐	_____

After listening

Thinking about what you learned about the topic

4 Think of the studying tips Sarah and Fredrick gave their younger brother. Which of these tips work for you? Which tips don't work for you? Support your answers with examples.

TIPS THAT WORK FOR ME

_____

_____

_____

_____

TIPS THAT DON'T WORK FOR ME

_____

_____

_____

_____

L-4

How Well
Do You Eat?

Before listening

Thinking about what you already know about the topic

1 What did you eat yesterday? Place the different foods you ate in the proper categories. Be specific (for example, 3 slices of bread).

Milk and dairy products: _____

Meat and alternates: _____

Breads and cereals: _____

Fruits and vegetables: _____

Other: _____

2 Complete the following statements.

The *Canadian Food Guide* recommends that teenagers eat the following daily servings:

_3-4_ servings of milk and dairy products _____ servings of meat and alternates

_____ servings of breads and cereals _____ servings of fruits and vegetables

Did you eat your daily recommended servings from each food group yesterday? _____

What percentage of your classmates did? _____

While listening

Asking yourself questions about the topic

3 Answer the following questions. Then, listen to the recording and write what is suggested in the text.

1. How can you make your favourite food better for you?

Me: _____

What the text said: _____

2. How should you order your hamburger? _____

Me: _____

What the text said: _____

3. What kind of pizza should you eat?

Me: _____

What the text said: _____

4. What should you eat as an after-school snack?

Me: _____

What the text said: _____

4 How did your answers compare to the suggestions made in the text? Place an X on the line to indicate your answer.

all the same   mostly the same   mostly different   totally different

After listening

> *Using the information you learned from the text*

5 In general, do you think you eat well? Explain by giving examples of your daily eating habits.

_____

_____

6 In view of what you've just heard in the text, what can you do to have healthier eating habits?

_____

_____

7 Students often complain about the food served in their school cafeterias. Work with a partner and plan a weekly menu for your school cafeteria. Keep the following restrictions in mind:

a) It must be food most students will like (food that tastes good).
b) It mustn't be expensive.
c) It must be healthy and well balanced (food from all four food groups).

Write up your menu on a sheet of paper and present it to another pair of students. Justify your choices.

WOOLLY
SLOPE-KEEPERS

In Quebec, more and more ski slopes are being used for mountain biking in the summer. So now the owners have to make sure that their slopes are maintained all year round. Most of them rely on expensive machinery, but others are discovering ingenious ways to ensure the maintenance of their ski resorts.

Before listening

Using the title and illustration to get the general idea of a text

1 First write down what these words remind you of:

Wool(ly): _____

Slope: _____

Keep(ers): _____

2 Before you listen to the text, look at the illustration and read the title. Explain what you think the text is about.

_____

_____

While listening

Listening for specific information

3 Now listen to the text and find two advantages of using sheep for the maintenance of ski slopes.

1. _____

2. _____

Identifying the sequence of events

4 Listen to the text again. Find the order in which these events took place in the story. Complete the sentences below.

a) Mr. Lavoie brought his sheep to Mont-Comi.
b) Mr. Levesque planned for the sheep to come back the next year.
c) Mr. Levesque hired Mr. Lavoie for the maintenance of his ski slopes.
d) The flock went back to Mr. Lavoie's pasture.
e) For two months, the sheep ate the grass and shrubs on the slopes.

The correct order is:

First, _____

Next, _____

Then, _____

After that, _____

Finally, _____

After listening

Retelling the information in your own words
Answering the questions "Who?" "What?" "Where?"
"When?" and "How?"

5 Tell the story in your own words. Make sure your text has all the information needed to answer these questions: **Who** is the story about? **What** happened? **Where** did the story take place? **When** did it take place? **How** does it end? You can also add some details.

_____

_____

_____

_____

_____

_____

A Different KIND OF JOB

Before listening

> *Using illustrations to understand a text*

1 Here are some words related to an interesting career called volcanology. Match each word with the correct illustration. Write its number in the box.

1. Volcano
2. Earthquake
3. Computers
4. Lava
5. Eruption
6. Rocks

> *Thinking about what you already know about the topic*
> *Asking questions about the topic*

2 **a)** What do you know about volcanoes and volcanology, the study of volcanoes? Write the information below.

b) Prepare three questions you would like to ask a volcanologist about his or her job. Write your questions on page 13.

THREE THINGS I KNOW	DOES THE TEXT MENTION THIS?	
	YES	NO
1. _____	☐	☐
2. _____	☐	☐
3. _____	☐	☐

MY QUESTIONS	DOES THE TEXT ANSWER THIS?	
	YES	NO
1. _____	☐	☐
2. _____	☐	☐
3. _____	☐	☐

While listening

3 Listen to the text *A Different Kind of Job* and indicate whether the points and questions you wrote above are mentioned by making a check mark in the appropriate column.

> *Thinking of the information you want to find*

4 Look at the following questions about being a volcanologist. Listen to the text a second time and write the appropriate answer.

1. What does a volcanologist do? _____

_____

2. What can a volcanologist use to collect important information?

_____

3. If you want to become a volcanologist, which courses should you take at school?

_____

After listening

> *Thinking about what you learned about the topic*

5 Write what you learned about volcanologists.

_____

_____

_____

THE DAWNING
OF YAWNING

People yawn all day long, from the moment they wake up till the time they go to bed. Have you ever wondered about what makes you yawn and why almost every time you see someone else yawn you start yawning too? Do you have any idea of what makes yawns so contagious? And does reading this text about yawning make you yawn?

Before listening

> *Using the title and illustration to get a general idea of a text*

1 Look at the title and the illustration. What do you think the general idea of the text will be?

a) Various facts about yawning
b) Boring situations that make people yawn
c) The relationship between the brain and yawning
d) Discovering why yawning is contagious

While listening

> *Listening for the general idea of a text*

2 Now listen to the text to see if your answer to number 1 was correct.

3 Read the sentences and notice the words in bold. Listen to the text and circle True or False according to the information you hear.

1. We **yawn** when we **see** another person **yawning**.	*True*	*False*
2. We **yawn** when we find something **dull**.	*True*	*False*
3. People **yawn** when they **feel uncomfortable**.	*True*	*False*
4. Some **researchers** have been **studying yawning**.	*True*	*False*
5. **Scientists** observed that we can **yawn** up to **seventy-six times an hour**.	*True*	*False*
6. **Prehistoric people** used **yawning** to **communicate**.	*True*	*False*
7. **Only** our **mouth stretches** when we yawn.	*True*	*False*
8. **Yawning** is **contagious**.	*True*	*False*

After listening

4 Use your own words to explain why experts think yawning is contagious. You can use the information from the previous activity.

_____

_____

_____

_____

_____

_____

_____

_____

_____

_____

_____

⌐-8 USING COMPUTERS
IN THE CLASSROOM

There is a growing debate in education today on the place we should give to the use of computers in the classroom. Should children begin working on computers in elementary school, or should teaching computers be reserved for the higher levels, like CEGEP or university?

Before listening

> Thinking about the topic of a text

1 Read the following statements. Indicate next to each one whether you think the statement is *for* or *against* learning computers in elementary school. Discuss your answers with a classmate.

   a) We don't need to take computer classes in grade school.   _____

   b) We should learn at an early age.   _____

   c) You can succeed in life without learning to use a computer.   _____

   d) Sooner is better.   _____

2 Think of an argument *for* learning to use computers at an early age. Then think of an argument *against* it.

   For: _____

   _____

   Against: _____

   _____

While listening

> Listening for specific information

3 Listen to what a group of Secondary 5 students had to say on the subject. Decide whether each student is *for* or *against* learning to use computers at an early age. Choose the statement that supports your answer. Follow the example.

STATEMENTS:
a) I would have liked a computer class when I was younger.
b) You only need a computer class if the job you want to do later on requires using a computer.
c) Learning computers in elementary school gives everyone an equal opportunity.
d) You don't need special courses to play computer games.
e) It is better for students to learn to use computers at an early age.
f) It is more important to learn to read and write properly than to learn to use a computer.

	FOR	AGAINST	STATEMENT
Student 1	☒	☐	*e) It is better for students to learn to use computers at an early age.*
Student 2	☐	☐	
Student 3	☐	☐	
Student 4	☐	☐	
Student 5	☐	☐	
Student 6	☐	☐	

After listening

> *Using what you learned to express your own ideas*

4 How do you feel about learning computers at an early age? Are you *for* or *against?* Support your answer with at least two arguments.

☐ I am *for* because   ☐ I am *against* because

Argument 1: _____

_____

_____

Argument 2: _____

_____

_____

IS IT
TRUE LOVE?

We sometimes have difficulty interpreting the feelings we have for others. Here is some information to help you recognize the differences between friendship, love and infatuation.

Before listening

> *Thinking about what you already know about the topic*

1 Write down what you know about these different types of relationships.

1. Friendship: _____

_____

2. Love: _____

_____

3. Infatuation: _____

_____

While listening

> *Listening for the general idea of a text*

2 Listen to the text. Choose a title for each part of the text. Justify your answers by writing two key words that helped you choose each title.

a) What Real Friendship is About   **b)** Looking for a Boyfriend/Girlfriend

c) The Meaning of True Love   **d)** Is it Love or Infatuation?

	TITLE	KEYWORDS
Part **1**:	_____	_____
Part **2**:	_____	_____
Part **3**:	_____	_____

Read the words and definitions below. Match each word with the correct definition. Then listen to the text again to check your answers.

Part **1**: Unrealistic

a) when we don't like someone
b) when we believe that something is possible when it's not
c) when we are relaxed

Part **2**: Commitment

a) when we are not careful
b) when we know about a person's future plans
c) when we give the support that we promised

Part **3**: Caring

a) when we don't respect someone
b) when we feel physically attracted
c) when we are attentive to someone else's needs

After listening

4 Think about yourself and the people around you. Why do you consider some of them as friends and others as acquaintances? Give examples of how you behave with your real friends.

_____

_____

_____

_____

_____

_____

L-10

IT'S ALL
IN YOUR NOSE

Before listening

> Linking the title to the topic of a text

1 This recording is about one of the five senses: taste. Think about the title and the topic and decide which of the following statements the text will focus on.

	MY PREDICTION	THE TEXT SAID
1. You need your nose to smell.	☐	☐
2. Taste is the most important of the senses.	☐	☐
3. You taste with your nose.	☐	☐
4. You cannot survive without a nose.	☐	☐
5. Taste and smell are closely linked.	☐	☐

While listening

2 Now listen to the recording and check out your prediction.

> Focusing on key words to understand a text

3 Here is a list of words from the recording. Choose from the words below and write a sentence that gives the essential information of the text.

ate	meal	mouth	breath
aroma	nose	water	taste
food	brain	distinguish	salty
pinch	sweet	sniffing	sensation

4 Look at the following statements. Listen to the tape again. Which statement or statements **do not** correspond to the information stated in the text?

1. Your mouth can detect sweet and sour tastes. ☐
2. You distinguish most flavours with your taste buds. ☐
3. You sniff the aroma of the food you eat. ☐
4. Without the use of your nose, most food tastes the same. ☐
5. You don't need your nose to identify strong spices like ginger or cinnamon. ☐

After listening

Identifying the sequence of events

5 Here are the steps involved in identifying the various flavours of food we eat. First, match the different parts of each sentence (A + B + C). Then, write the steps in the correct order. Use the illustrations for help.

A	B	C
The brain	eat or drink	the part of our nose that contains the olfactory nerves.
The food odours	send	a message to the brain.
We	associates the aroma with	different foods.
The olfactory nerves	reach	a flavour we have tasted in the past.

- _____
- _____
- _____
- _____

PARENTS
WHO SPY

Parents know that teenagers have to live their own lives. While some parents accept the fact that teens sometimes have to learn from their own mistakes, others prefer to secretly watch over their teens to make sure nothing bad happens to them. Should spying be considered as proof of parental love, or is it simply an invasion of privacy?

Before listening

> *Using the title and illustrations to get the general idea of a text*

1 Look at the illustration. What do you think a **spy** is?

_____

2 Give an example of what a parent can do to spy on a teenager.

_____

While listening

> *Listening for specific information*

3 Listen to the six texts. For each one, write in whether the speaker is *for* or *against* parents spying on their teens.

Text **1:** _____   Text **4:** _____

Text **2:** _____   Text **5:** _____

Text **3:** _____   Text **6:** _____

4 According to the texts, what did the parents do to invade their teens' privacy?

Text **1:** _____

Text **2:** _____

Text **3:** _____

Text **4:** _____

Text **5:** _____

Text **6:** _____

After listening

> Using the information you learned from the text

5 Write two arguments *for* and two arguments *against* parents who spy.
Use the ideas from the texts you heard.

For parents who spy: _____

_____

_____

Against parents who spy: _____

_____

_____

6 What would you say to parents who spy on their teens? _____

_____

_____

_____

_____

_____

_____

_____

_____

_____

L-12 UFO
ENCOUNTERS

Do you believe there is some form of life on other planets? Well, some people have reported seeing UFOs while they were driving on isolated roads in the middle of the night. A few of them even declare that they have been kidnapped by aliens, and that these beings from space conducted painful experiments on them in order to get information on how the human body functions.

Before listening

Focusing on familiar words
Guessing the meaning of unfamiliar words

1 Match each word with its definition.

1. aliens   ☐ producing a person, animal or thing artificially

2. cloning   ☐ a sleep-like state

3. abduct   ☐ creatures from other planets

4. abductees   ☐ to take someone away by force

5. hypnosis   ☐ victims of kidnapping

Focusing on key words to understand a text

2 Circle the phrases in the box that seem to state facts, and underline the ones that state opinions.

Ms. Collings remembers that • it happened in 1947 • over Mount Rainier
people think that • for fifty years • that might explain why
Mr. Carpenter is a psychiatric social worker • it's scary to imagine
a theory going around • these people might suffer from a sleep disorder

While listening

3 Listen to the sentences. Indicate in the table which ones state *facts* and which ones state *opinions*.

	1	2	3	4	5	6	7	8	9	10
FACT	☐	☐	☐	☐	☐	☐	☐	☐	☐	☐
OPINION	☐	☐	☐	☐	☐	☐	☐	☐	☐	☐

> *Brainstorming for key words*

4 Before listening to the text again, write down some key words that can help you differentiate the *general* from the *specific* information.

General: _____

Specific: _____

> *Focusing on key words to understand a text*

5 Listen to the recording again. In the table, identify which sentences are *specific* and which are *general*.

	1	2	3	4	5	6	7	8	9	10
SPECIFIC	☐	☐	☐	☐	☐	☐	☐	☐	☐	☐
GENERAL	☐	☐	☐	☐	☐	☐	☐	☐	☐	☐

After listening

> *Expressing your opinion about what you heard*

6 Do you believe in UFOs, and that some people have actually seen them?
Do you believe that some humans have been abducted by aliens?
If not, why do you think people tell such stories? Explain your answers.

_____

_____

_____

Buzz-
SLAP-SLAP!

Ah! Summer! A time to kick back and relax after a busy year of homework, tests and teachers. It would be the most perfect time of the year if it weren't for a tiny pest that has an annoying way of making its presence felt. Every year, thousands of mosquitoes find their way to your arms, legs and ankles. These insects are literally a pain in the neck. So, how can you protect yourself and have a bite-free summer?

Before listening

> *Brainstorming on the topic of a text*

1 Work with a partner and think of different ways you can protect yourself from mosquito attacks this summer.

_____

_____

_____

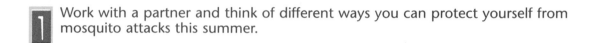

While listening

2 Now listen to the recording. Were any of the solutions you suggested mentioned in the text?

☐ Most of my suggestions were mentioned in the text.

☐ Some of my suggestions were mentioned in the text.

☐ None of my suggestions were mentioned in the text.

Circle the answers you had in common with the text.

> *Listening for the general idea of a text*

3 The recording you have just listened to has no title. Think of an appropriate title and write it in at the top of page 27.

> *Organizing the information you learned about the topic*

4 Listen to the text a second time. Use the following form to organize the information you hear.

TITLE: _____

WHY THEY ATTACK

_____

_____

WHERE THEY LIVE

_____

WHERE THEY LAY EGGS

_____

_____

WHAT ATTRACTS MOSQUITOES

_____

WAYS TO PROTECT YOURSELF

Keep the lawn short and the bushes well trimmed.

_____

_____

_____

_____

After listening

> *Retelling the information in your own words*

5 Use the information listed in number 4 to say what you have learned from the text.

_____

_____

_____

_____

_____

> *Expressing your opinion about what you heard*

6 This text gave some tips on protecting yourself from mosquitoes. Do all the suggestions mentioned in the text seem realistic to you? Explain your answer.

_____

_____

_____

_____

_____

WHITE-WATER
RAFTING

For most people, summer is a good time to relax and enjoy relatively peaceful sports like swimming and bicycling. But for some fearless adventurers, summer is also a season filled with excitement and hair-raising experiences.

Before listening

> *Thinking about what you already know and what you want to know about the topic*

1 Write what you already know about white-water rafting.

_____

_____

2 Write what you would like to know about white-water rafting.

_____

_____

part 1
While listening

> *Focusing on key words*

3 Listen to the text and circle the information you wrote in numbers 1 and 2 that corresponds to what you hear.

4 Name some of the tasks that a white-water rafting guide does.

_____

_____

_____

After listening

5 Use your own words to explain what a guide will do to make sure your ride is as safe as possible. Write at least three things.

_____

_____

_____

part II
While listening

6 Listen to the second part of the text. Identify the classifications of the rapids according to the information you hear.

	CLASSIFICATION	DESCRIPTION NUMBER
Classes **I** and **II**:	Very easy and easy	☐
Class **III**:	Medium	☐
Class **IV**:	Difficult	☐
Class **V**:	Very difficult	☐
Class **VI**:	Unrunnable or portage	☐

After listening

7 Write what you learned about white-water rafting.

_____

_____

_____

⊔-15 IT'S ALL RIGHT
TO BE LEFT

1 Are you right-handed or left-handed? Here is a fun test to see if you are mostly right-handed or left-handed. Circle the answer that best describes you.

1. When you peel a banana, which hand holds the banana?

2. Which hand do you use to wipe a spill off the floor?

3. When you put your books in your school bag, which hand holds the books?

4. When you cut an apple, which hand holds the apple?

5. Which hand are you using to answer these questions?

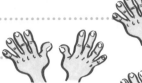

> If you answered *right* for numbers **2**, **3** and **5** and *left* for numbers **1** and **4**, you are probably right-handed. You are probably left-handed if you answered the reverse.

Before listening

> *Thinking about the topic of a text*

2 Try to answer the following questions before listening to the text.

1. What percentage of the population is left-handed?

   a) 10% **b)** 25% **c)** 50%

2. Which of these tasks do most left-handed people find difficult?

   a) using a can opener **b)** using scissors **c)** screwing in a light bulb

While listening

> *Verifying your answers*

3 Now listen to the text *It's All Right to Be Left* and check to see if your guesses were right. Make the necessary changes to your answers.

4 Listen to the text again and decide whether each of the numbered statements is a *fact* or an *opinion*. Write the word or group of words that helped you identify the statements of opinion.

	FACT	OPINION	KEY WORDS
1.	☐	☐	
2.	☐	☐	
3.	☐	☐	
4.	☐	☐	
5.	☐	☐	
6.	☐	☐	

After listening

5 Write the thing that surprised you the most about being left-handed.

_____

_____

_____

6 The Left-Right Challenge

Choose one of the following challenges and see how you do.

a) Place your watch on your right arm and set your watch one hour forward.
b) Take your scissors in the hand opposite to the one you normally use and try to cut a circle.

Did you find this easy or difficult to do? Explain.

_____

_____

_____

_____

TO BE OR NOT TO BE

PART OF THE COOL CROWD

Being part of a group can be really awesome, but if you want to hang out with the most popular kids in school, you may have to make major changes in your life. For some teens, being in the coolest group means everything.

Before listening

> Using the title to get the general idea of a text

1 Read the title and answer the question: What is the general idea of this text?

a) Deciding whether to be with the "in" crowd.
b) It's really exciting to be part of a cool group.
c) Some "in" teens can really be rude to other people.
d) Old friends can never be replaced.

While listening

> Focusing on key words to find specific information

2 Read the sentences and underline the key words. Then, listen to the text. Circle true or false according to what you hear in the text.

1. Elizabeth wasn't part of the cool group last year.	*True*	*False*
2. Now she's part of the group only because her parents have money.	*True*	*False*
3. One of the advantages of being with popular kids is that she can date good-looking boys.	*True*	*False*

3 Listen to the text again and answer the following questions.

1. What are two of the things Elizabeth did to become part of the cool crowd?

_____

_____

2. Why does Elizabeth say her new friends are rude?

_____

3. What are the disadvantages of being with the coolest kids?

_____

4. What are two other ways to say "cool crowd"?

_____

After listening

Expressing your opinion about what you heard

4 Write a short essay reflecting on the question at the end of the text: "Is popularity really worth all this?"

_____

_____

_____

_____

_____

_____

_____

_____

_____

_____

_____

_____

_____

_____

_____

_____

_____

_____

_____

_____

More Tips, Tricks and Strategies to Help Me Become a Better Listener

READING ACTIVITIES
STRATEGIES FOR READING

Before reading

Predict what the text will say by...

Brainstorming for key words
Relating the topic of a text to yourself
Thinking about what you already know and want to know about the topic
Using the context to guess the meaning of unfamiliar words
Using the title and illustrations to find the topic of a text
Using the title, subtitles, captions and illustrations to get the general idea of a text

While reading

Monitor your comprehension by...

Focusing on cognates to understand a text
Focusing on key words to get the general idea of a text
Focusing on key words to find specific information
Highlighting the information you need
Identifying the sequence of events
Looking for specific information
Looking for the main idea of a text by focusing on the topic
Looking up the definitions of unfamiliar words
Organizing the information you learned about a topic
Picturing things in your mind
Stopping after each paragraph to think about what you're reading
Using illustrations to understand a text
Using the context to guess the meaning of unfamiliar words

After reading

Verify your comprehension by...

Asking yourself questions about the text
Asking questions about what you still want to know about the topic
Expressing your opinion about the topic
Identifying the sequence of events
Relating the information in the text to what you already know about the topic
Using the information you learned from the text
Using the information from the text to express an opinion

THAT VERY
FIRST CAR

Before reading

Using the title and illustrations to find the topic of a text

1 Look at the title of the text and the illustrations on the next page. Which of the following statements do you think is the most accurate? Explain your choice.

1. This text talks about the first cars ever invented. . . . . ☐

Reason: _____

_____

2. This text talks about the difficulties of owning a car for the first time. . . . . ☐

Reason: _____

_____

3. This text describes different dream cars teenagers would like to have. . . . ☐

Reason: _____

_____

4. This text describes the first cars some people have owned. . . . . ☐

Reason: _____

_____

5. This text describes the importance of owning a car when you are a teenager. ☐

Reason: _____

_____

While reading

Picturing things in your mind

2 Now read the following text to check your answer to number 1. As you read, highlight the words that describe each car.

That Very First Car

Here you are. It's your last year of high school. You probably already have your driver's license or are in the process of getting it. Soon you will be looking to buy your first car. That is quite a commitment for anyone to make. There are the payments to consider, the insurance, the upkeep and the rising cost of gasoline. Also, finding a car to suit your budget is no easy task. More often than not, a first car is far from being a dream car. Just ask your parents. Still, nothing can compare to that sense of pride you have when you take your wheels out for that first spin around the block, no matter what kind of car you buy or what your car may look like. Here is what a group of parents had to say about their first car.

RICKY'S MOM:

My first car was a disaster. It needed more oil than it did gasoline. It would burn through oil in no time at all. It was so bad that my brother would bring me used oil from the tugboat he worked on. Every day I had to check the oil and fill up the car with the tugboat oil. I didn't mind, though, because whenever I was in a parking lot with the hood of the car open checking the oil, some guy would come around offering to help. It was great!

CAROLE'S DAD:

I remember my first car well. I didn't have much money to buy a fancy car. In fact, I didn't have much money to buy a not-so-fancy car. The only thing I could afford was a two-door sedan that had a leaky roof. The only way I could think of to keep the rain out was to put a canoe on the top of the car. I spent an entire year with that canoe on my car. People thought I was really into camping, when actually, I was simply trying to stay dry.

KARINE'S MOM:

The first car I ever bought was unbelievably rusty. It really needed a good paint job, and that was something I simply couldn't afford. So one day, my girlfriends and I decided to paint my car. We set up in my dad's driveway, and with our rollers and our paintbrushes we gave that car a new look. I remember the expression on my dad's face when he saw that we had used latex paint. I couldn't see the big deal until the first time it rained on my newly painted car. There were streaks of paint all over the driveway.

ALAN'S DAD:

My first car was a lime-green Bug. Sometimes the doors would stick and we had to climb into it or out of it through the sunroof. During the holidays, my friends and I decorated my car with Christmas lights. We actually put the lights inside the car. I plugged them into the car lighter. We certainly got a lot of funny looks that year.

3 What was the first car each person bought? Choose the right illustration.

Ricky's mom: _____   Karine's mom: _____

Carole's dad: _____   Alan's dad: _____

After reading

4 Look at the following questions, then read the story by Ricky's mom again to find the answers.

1. What was wrong with Ricky's mother's car?

_____

_____

2. What kind of oil did she use in her car?

_____

_____

3. What happened every time Ricky's mother checked the oil in her car?

_____

_____

4. Did she hate checking the oil in her car? Explain.

_____

_____

5
- Pair up with a classmate.
- Each one chooses a different car story and prepares three questions about it. Indicate which story you are asking about.
- Exchange books with your partner and answer each other's questions.

STORY: _____

Q: _____

_____

A: _____

_____

Q: _____

_____

A: _____

_____

Q: _____

_____

A: _____

_____

6 If you had to choose one of the cars described in the text as your very first car, which one would you choose? What would be your second choice? Which car would you never choose? Explain your choices.

My first choice: _____

_____

_____

_____

_____

_____

My second choice: _____

_____

_____

_____

_____

_____

I would never choose: _____

_____

_____

_____

_____

_____

_____

READING

That Very First Car

YOUR LIFE
IS IN YOUR HANDS

The lines in our hands change as we get older. Some people believe that these changes reflect the events that take place in our lives. Others believe that these lines hold clues to our personality, temperament and destiny.

Before reading

> *Relating the topic of a text to yourself*

1 Complete the following chart to get a profile of your character traits.

MY PERSONALITY ANALYSIS

	ALWAYS	OFTEN	SOMETIMES	RARELY	NEVER
a) I am affectionate	☐	☐	☐	☐	☐
b) I am impulsive	☐	☐	☐	☐	☐
c) I am warm and friendly	☐	☐	☐	☐	☐
d) I am optimistic	☐	☐	☐	☐	☐
e) I am understanding	☐	☐	☐	☐	☐
f) I am ambitious	☐	☐	☐	☐	☐
g) I work hard	☐	☐	☐	☐	☐
h) I have a good memory	☐	☐	☐	☐	☐
i) I am family oriented	☐	☐	☐	☐	☐
j) I am creative	☐	☐	☐	☐	☐
k) I am determined	☐	☐	☐	☐	☐

> *Scanning a text to find specific information*

2 Look through the text to find the sentences that describe your strongest character traits. Underline the words that apply to your personality.

While reading

> *Highlighting the information you need*

READING

Your Life is in Your Hands

3 Read the text in detail. Look at the lines in your hand as you read.
Highlight the physical descriptions that correspond to the lines in your own palm.

Your Life is in Your Hands

How much do you know about palmistry? Here's a quick summary of the meaning of the six most prominent lines in your palms. You can find out if your hands tell the truth about your personality by looking at your dominant hand, the one you write with.

1 THE HEART LINE:

If the right end is under your middle finger, it means that you are more driven by your head than by your heart. A short, straight line indicates that you have trouble showing affection. A long line indicates that you're lucky in love. A strong line means you are a warm person, whereas a weak line implies that you are reluctant to give your love.

2 THE HEAD LINE:

A long, strong line means you are very intelligent. If your head line drops sharply down, it means that you have a great memory. If it curves down from your index finger to under your pinky, you are probably spontaneous.

3 THE LIFE LINE:

If you have a very long life line, it might mean that you'll live to a ripe old age. If it's long and clear, you won't have any major problems with your health. If it goes up through your heart line, you are a very ambitious person.

4 THE WORK LINE:

The stronger the line, the harder you work to succeed. It also indicates that you understand people well. A short line means you might experience problems at work.

5 THE FAMILY LINE:

It's the line around the base of the thumb. The stronger it is, the more family-oriented you are.

6 THE DESTINY LINE:

It goes upward from the base of your hand. A weak line means you have no clear idea of what you want to do with your life. A double line indicates creativity, success and prosperity. If it's clear and goes to the base of your middle finger, you're on a slow but steady path toward success.

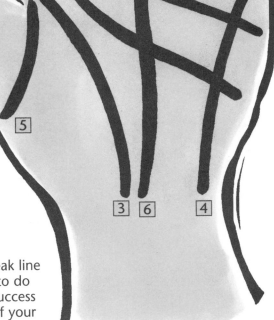

After reading

Using the information you learned from the text

4 Write a description of who you are supposed to be based on the information in the text.

Example: *According to the text, I have trouble showing affection and I'm very intelligent.*

_____

_____

_____

_____

_____

_____

_____

5 Use a blue pen to underline the information in number 4 that you believe to be true about yourself. Use a red pen to underline the information you consider to be false.

6 Write your opinion about palmistry. Give at least two examples that support your opinion.

_____

_____

_____

_____

_____

_____

_____

_____

_____

_____

_____

_____

 WHEN

SYLVIA DATES

Before reading

> Thinking about the topic of a text

1 Which of the following situations would be a dream date for you?

☐ Driving around in a fancy sports car

☐ Going to an expensive restaurant

☐ Going to a rock concert to hear your favourite band/group

☐ A date with a top model/favourite actor

2 Which would be your worst nightmare date?

☐ Your date invites you to a fancy restaurant and forgets to bring money.

☐ The car you are in runs out of gas and you and your date have to push it to the nearest gas station.

☐ Your parents force you to bring along your kid brother or sister.

☐ Your parents accompany you.

Planning a date can make even the calmest person feel nervous. Imagine what planning three dates at the same time can do to you. That is exactly what Sylvia did one fine Saturday. Read all about it in her e-mail letter to her Australian pen pal Karly.

While reading

> Focusing on key words to understand a text

3 Certain words (or groups of words) in the text give information about the order in which the events happened. Take a pencil and underline these words as you read. Look at the underlined words in the text for an example.

READING

When Sylvia Dates

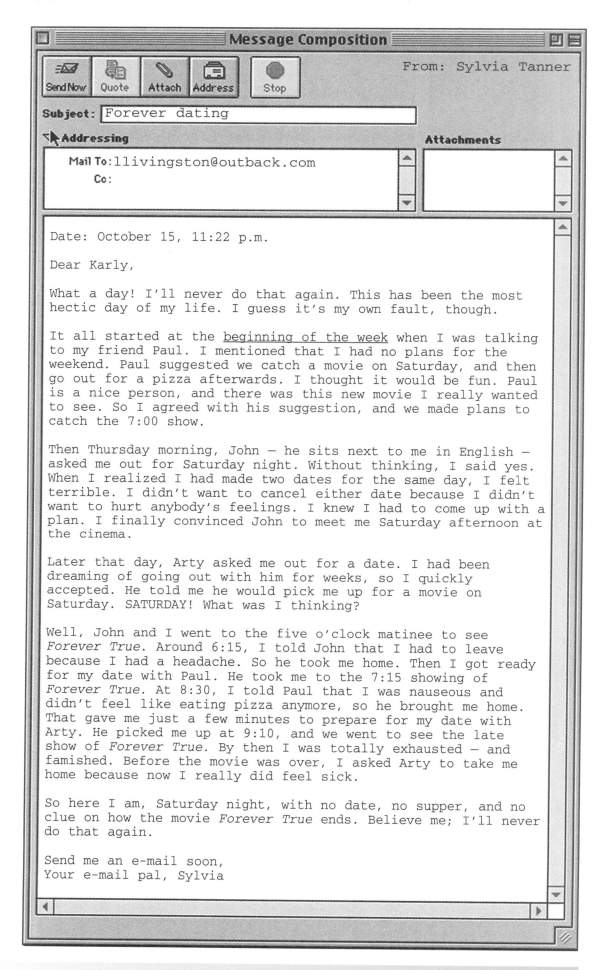

Message Composition

Send Now   Quote   Attach   Address   Stop

From: Sylvia Tanner

Subject: Forever dating

Addressing

Mail To: llivingston@outback.com
Cc:

Attachments

Date: October 15, 11:22 p.m.

Dear Karly,

What a day! I'll never do that again. This has been the most hectic day of my life. I guess it's my own fault, though.

It all started at the beginning of the week when I was talking to my friend Paul. I mentioned that I had no plans for the weekend. Paul suggested we catch a movie on Saturday, and then go out for a pizza afterwards. I thought it would be fun. Paul is a nice person, and there was this new movie I really wanted to see. So I agreed with his suggestion, and we made plans to catch the 7:00 show.

Then Thursday morning, John — he sits next to me in English — asked me out for Saturday night. Without thinking, I said yes. When I realized I had made two dates for the same day, I felt terrible. I didn't want to cancel either date because I didn't want to hurt anybody's feelings. I knew I had to come up with a plan. I finally convinced John to meet me Saturday afternoon at the cinema.

Later that day, Arty asked me out for a date. I had been dreaming of going out with him for weeks, so I quickly accepted. He told me he would pick me up for a movie on Saturday. SATURDAY! What was I thinking?

Well, John and I went to the five o'clock matinee to see *Forever True*. Around 6:15, I told John that I had to leave because I had a headache. So he took me home. Then I got ready for my date with Paul. He took me to the 7:15 showing of *Forever True*. At 8:30, I told Paul that I was nauseous and didn't feel like eating pizza anymore, so he brought me home. That gave me just a few minutes to prepare for my date with Arty. He picked me up at 9:10, and we went to see the late show of *Forever True*. By then I was totally exhausted — and famished. Before the movie was over, I asked Arty to take me home because now I really did feel sick.

So here I am, Saturday night, with no date, no supper, and no clue on how the movie *Forever True* ends. Believe me; I'll never do that again.

Send me an e-mail soon,
Your e-mail pal, Sylvia

Looking for specific information

4 Decide whether the following statements are true or false. Correct the ones that are false by writing a new sentence below.

---

1. By Friday, Sylvia had no plans for the weekend.   *True*   *False*

---

2. Sylvia wanted to see the movie *Forever True*.   *True*   *False*

---

3. Sylvia went out with Paul before she went out with John.   *True*   *False*

---

4. On her date with Paul, Sylvia pretended to be nauseous.   *True*   *False*

---

5. Sylvia enjoyed the ending of the movie *Forever True*.   *True*   *False*

After reading

Identifying the sequence of events

5 Here is a scrambled list of the events that happened to Sylvia last week. Read the sentences and put them in chronological order.

- Think about which event came first.
- Think about which event came last.
- Which sentence goes before 1? After 1? Before and after 8? Before and after 7?

THE CORRECT ORDER IS:

| | | 1 | | | 8 | | | 7 | | |

1. John asks Sylvia for a date.
2. Sylvia feels sick.
3. Paul and Sylvia go to the cinema.
4. Sylvia goes home again.
5. Paul invites Sylvia to the cinema and for a pizza.
6. Sylvia dreams of going on a date with Arty.
7. Sylvia goes to the cinema with Arty.
8. Sylvia goes home.
9. Sylvia feels she has had a hectic day.
10. Sylvia and John go to the cinema.
11. Arty invites Sylvia to the cinema.

Making up a different ending to the text

6 Sylvia ended her day with no date and no supper. Work with a classmate and imagine a different ending to her day. Look at the suggestions if you need ideas.

- Imagine that the three boys are good friends, and they tell each other everything.
- Imagine that Arty arrives at Sylvia's house before Paul has left.
- Imagine that Sylvia feels fine on her date with Arty and watches the entire movie.

_____

_____

_____

_____

_____

_____

_____

_____

_____

_____

_____

_____

_____

_____

THE KING

OF HORROR

Before reading

> Thinking about what you already know about the topic

1 Answer these questions to find out how much you know about Stephen King.

	YES	No		YES	No
1. Is he married?	☐	☐	**4.** Is he Canadian?	☐	☐
2. Is he a writer?	☐	☐	**5.** Is he an actor?	☐	☐
3. Is he a movie producer?	☐	☐	**6.** Does he have any children?	☐	☐

While reading

> Focusing on key words

2 Read the scrambled sentences about Stephen King. As you read, underline the words that can be used to link two ideas together. For example: <u>and</u>, <u>then</u>.

The King of Horror

A. Then he discovered that writing was a good form of expression, and he started writing scary stories.

B. But Stephen has been called the King of Horror, so let's find out how he got such a title.

C. and to his family and friends, he is just a nice, ordinary man.

D. As a teenager, Stephen was quiet and shy.

E. After reading Stephen's first shocker, his friends encouraged him to continue,

F. Writers speak openly on issues they feel strongly about.

G. The American author Stephen King lives in the state of Maine with his wife and their three children,

H. and that was the beginning of the King of Horror's long and productive career.

3 Recreate the paragraph about Stephen King by writing the sentences in the correct order. Be careful! One sentence does not belong in the text.

_____

_____

_____

_____

_____

_____

_____

_____

_____

_____

_____

_____

_____

Now write the sentence that doesn't belong in the text: _____

_____

_____

After reading

Using the information you learned from the text

4 Go back to number 1 and correct your answers according to the information in the text.

5 Are you a Stephen King fan, or do you prefer another author? Fill in the information below about an author you like.

Author: _____

Nationality: _____

Other information: _____

6 Choose one of the books you enjoyed most by this author. Fill in the information below.

Title: _____

Type of book: _____

Names of the leading characters and what they do in the story:
(**Example:** *Ernest: gardener and assassin.*)

_____

_____

_____

_____

Description of the setting (where and when the story takes place):

_____

_____

_____

_____

Your general opinion of the book:

_____

_____

_____

_____

_____

_____

_____

_____

_____

_____

_____

_____

_____

READING

The King of Horror

MURPHY'S LAW
AND SCHOOL LIFE

Before reading

Skimming a text

 Look at the title and read only the first paragraph of the text. Complete the sentence below by circling the appropriate letter.

Murphy's Law is a theory…

a) about how to behave in school.

b) that says that if you are well prepared, nothing can go wrong.

c) that says that negative things will probably occur, even if you worked hard to avoid them.

d) about how a cafeteria functions.

Now, look at the following subtitles. Without reading the text, try to predict what each section will talk about.

MURPHY'S LAW AT EXAM TIME

_____

_____

_____

MURPHY'S LAW AT LUNCH TIME

_____

_____

_____

MURPHY'S LAW AND HOMEWORK

_____

_____

_____

MURPHY'S LAW IN THE CLASSROOM

_____

_____

_____

Murphy's Law and School Life

While reading

2 Now read the text carefully and check out your predictions.

> *Picturing things in your mind*

3 Look at the pictures and draw a line linking each one to the example it illustrates.

Murphy's Law and School Life

Have you ever planned a party, and no matter how much time you put into the preparation, no matter how much effort you put into the organization, you just knew something would go wrong? And it did! This is called the theory of Murphy's Law. Murphy's Law says, "If anything can go wrong, it will." In other words, no matter how much you plan, things probably won't go the way you want them to. For example: if you are waiting in line at the school cafeteria, the line next to yours will always move faster. If you change lines, the line you were in before will start to move faster. Such is life!

Here are some other examples of Murphy's Law.

MURPHY'S LAW AT EXAM TIME

- No matter how much you study, the teacher will always ask a question on something you didn't review.

  - Your pencil will break in a classroom with no pencil sharpeners, on a day you don't have extra pencils.

    - The amount of time you have to write your exam is inversely proportional to the level of difficulty of that exam.

MURPHY'S LAW AT LUNCH TIME

- When it's your turn to order, the food will be either cold, unavailable, or unrecognizable.

- The food you really want will cost 50¢ more than you have.

(continued)

MURPHY'S LAW AND HOMEWORK

- The one time that you forget to do your homework is the day your teacher will decide to check to see if it's done.

- The amount of homework you have to do is inversely proportional to the number of days you have to do it in.

- The day after you use the excuse "My dog ate my homework," your dog really will eat your homework.

MURPHY'S LAW IN THE CLASSROOM

- The teacher's fingernails will be one quarter of an inch longer than the chalk he or she is using.

- No matter where you sit, the student next to you will never have any paper, pens, or tissues.

- There will never be a snowstorm when you need one.

Some people believe that life is a series of events you simply cannot control. Other people say that it's up to individuals to control every aspect of their own lives. In either case, you have to consider one very important variable — Murphy's Law.

Is your life a series of Murphy's Laws?

4 Read the following law and describe a scene to illustrate it. Imagine that you are telling an illustrator exactly what to draw. Give as many details as possible.

There will never be a snowstorm when you need one.

_____

_____

_____

_____

_____

Now compare your description to a classmate's.

5 Explain the following examples of Murphy's Law.

a) *The food you really want will cost 50¢ more than you have.*

_____

_____

_____

b) *The amount of homework you have to do is inversely proportional to the number of days you have to do it in.*

_____

_____

_____

6 Which example of Murphy's Law best represents the following situation?

I hate it when people want to borrow my things.

_____

_____

After reading

> *Using the information you learned from the text*

7 Work with a partner and create another example of Murphy's Law for school life. Choose from the following topics.

- Murphy's Law and team sports
- Murphy's Law at recess
- Murphy's Law in gym class
- Murphy's Law and school life in general

_____

_____

_____

_____

USING SENSE, NOT CENTS

HOW TO CELEBRATE YOUR PROM WISELY

 Before reading

> *Thinking about what you already know about the topic*

1 The last year of high school can be a very expensive year for many students. Which of the following items do you intend to buy this year?

☐ Yearbook ☐ School ring

☐ Souvenir T-shirt ☐ Prom tickets ☐ Graduation pictures

Which item do you think will be the most costly? _____

Which item will be the least costly? _____

2 How much do you expect to pay for your prom? $ _____

3 What suggestions would you give students who would like to keep their prom expenses low?

_____

_____

_____

_____

> *Thinking about what you want to know about the topic*

4 Which of the following points would you like to know more about regarding your prom?

How to earn money to cover prom expenses	☐
How to organize your preparation time and your money	☐
Finding options to buying expensive clothing and accessories	☐
How to limit prom expenses	☐
How to have fun on prom night	☐
How to make a prom budget	☐

 Now read the text to see if it gives you information on the points you checked off.

Using Sense, Not Cents: How to Celebrate Your Prom Wisely

For many students, the last year of high school is synonymous with graduation and celebration. Prom night is certainly an important event in many students' lives, but the cost of the affair can be more than most teenagers can handle. However, with careful planning, a good budget and a little creativity, your memories will be about your prom night, not about how much you spent to get there.

1) Understanding the difference between how much you want to spend and how much you can afford to spend is the first step to spending wisely. That means preparing a budget. **2) First, decide how much money you have to spend for all your graduation expenses.** Then, draw up a list of all the clothing and accessories you would like for your prom. Write an estimated price next to each item. Add to this the cost of transportation and prom tickets, as well as an amount for the pre-prom and after-prom parties. Make sure you include the cost of graduation pictures, rings, yearbook and any other graduation memento your class or school plans to offer. These items bring up the total cost of your graduation budget.

The next thing to do is to eliminate from your list any items you can do without. For example, do you really need a hat to accessorize your outfit, and is it absolutely necessary to show up at your prom in a limousine? If you find that your list includes only the bare minimum but you are still way over budget, then reduce the amount you are prepared to spend on the various items. Clothes don't have to cost a lot to look great.

3) Another way to keep costs down is to use your imagination. Instead of renting a limo, clean and decorate the family car. Ask a parent or an older sibling to act as chauffeur. The effect will be just as stunning. **4) Before buying expensive new clothes and jewellery, look in your closet and see what you already have that you can use.** Ask family members and friends if they have anything you could borrow, such as costume jewellery, gloves, shawls or other accessories. **5) If you need to find shoes to match your gown or suit, then tint or dye an old pair instead of buying new ones.** Look into second-hand shops; you might be surprised at some of the treasures you can find there. There is no limit to what you can do to give yourself a special and unique look, once you set your mind to it.

To really save, it's best to start planning a few months in advance. Take the time to comparison shop. **6) Watch for sales and special discount days at your favourite shops.** Compare the price of renting a dress or suit with the cost of buying something new. Shop around for accessories, flowers and transportation. **7) There are plenty of good bargains out there, you just have to take the time to find them.**

Finally, don't wait till the last minute to start saving up for your prom expenses. As soon as you have made up your mind to go, start putting those dollars aside. Always keep an eye on your list of prom expenses and stick to the limit you set yourself. Remember — control your prom expenses; don't let them control you.

Focusing on cognates to understand a text

6 Look in the text to find the words that correspond to the following definitions.

1. having the same meaning as another word or expression _____

2. a list of all your projected expenses _____

3. an article enumerated in a series _____

4. a person whose job is driving a car _____

Did you find this exercise easy or difficult to do? _____

What did these words have in common?

_____

_____

_____

7 Words that resemble and have the same meaning as words in your mother tongue are called cognates. List as many cognates as you can from the text. Compare your list with a classmate's. Complete each other's lists.

_____

_____

_____

_____

Organizing the information you learned about a topic

8 To understand a text, there are a few things you should think about:

- the topic
- the topic sentence
- distinguishing between general information and specific information

a) The title usually gives you an idea of the **topic**—or subject—of the text. Look at the title and, in your own words, write the topic of the text.

_____

_____

_____

b) The **topic sentence** of a text is the sentence that gives you the main idea of the text. It is usually at the beginning or the end of the text, but it can be in the middle. The topic sentence should mention the topic explicitly.

- Underline all the sentences in the text that mention the topic.
- Choose the underlined sentence that gives the best summary of the text. This is the topic sentence. Write the first three words on the line below.

_____

c) Some sentences in a text are **general** observations or general ideas about the topic. Other sentences give **specific** details or examples that explain the general observations. Some texts go from general observations to specific details. Others go from specific details to general observations. A topic sentence is an example of a general idea.

- Look at the sentences in bold. Decide whether each sentence represents a general idea or gives specific information that explains or supports a general idea in the text. Put G for general and S for specific.

1	2	3	4	5	6	7
☐	☐	☐	☐	☐	☐	☐

After reading

Thinking about what you learned about the topic

9 What suggestions from the text do you think you might use in planning for your prom? Explain.

_____
_____
_____
_____
_____

What suggestions will you ignore? Explain.

_____
_____
_____
_____
_____
_____

Using Sense, Not Cents...

GUY
TALK

Before reading

Brainstorming for key words

---

1 **a)** Write words and expressions you use to indicate that you are *for* a certain situation.

_____

_____

b) Now write words and expressions you use to indicate that you are *against* something.

_____

_____

_____

In today's society, it's no longer up to the boys to ask girls out on a date. Girls also take a leading role in the dating game. In this text, you will read how four guys feel about girls who make the first move.

Skimming a text

---

2 Read only the **first and last sentence** of each section of the text. For each young man, write down whether you think he is *for* or *against* girls making the first move. Explain your answers.

Section I: I think Chris is _____

_____

_____

Section II: In my opinion, Don _____

_____

_____

Section III: _____

_____

_____

Section IV: _____

_____

_____

> *Focusing on key words to get the general idea of a text*

3 Read the four sections of the text carefully and look at the choice of subtitles in the box below. Choose the most appropriate subtitle for each section. Explain your answers by writing two key words from each text.

> • **Like Father, Like Son**   • **Go For It!**
> • **On With the New**   • **Approach Me, Please!**

Section I (Chris): _____

_____

Section II: (Don): _____

_____

Section III (Mario): _____

_____

Section IV (Yves): _____

_____

GUY TALK

Section I (Chris): I love it when a girl takes charge and asks me to go out with her. I'm a shy guy so I always worry that if I go talk to a girl, only stupid things will come out of my mouth, and she'll think I'm an idiot. This is why I truly appreciate a girl who is outgoing enough to come up and talk to me first. I also think it's very flattering.

Section II (Don): My first reaction is to say that it turns me off when a girl wants to force a situation. On the other hand, I think girls should be modern, and that means they can be assertive and show us how they feel. So as far as I'm concerned, I guess I can say that I don't really care who makes the first move. What truly matters is that we get to know each other better and see how well we get along.

Section III (Mario): It's great because it's a sign that she is interested in me. I like it when a girl knows what she wants and makes the first move. It also takes off some of the pressure from us guys because most of the time, girls just wait for us to talk to them first. If she is confident enough to come up to a guy, she's probably also independent, and that's something I like in a girl.

Section IV (Yves): I definitely don't appreciate that in a girl. When she comes on to me first, I think she's aggressive. Maybe I'm old-fashioned, but I prefer to have control over my dating. Personally, I'm not comfortable with a girl who is too direct because I think she'll want to control everything else in the relationship.

READING

Guy Talk

Scanning for specific information

4 Go back to the text. Move your eyes quickly through the four sections to find the words the guys used about girls who make the first move. Underline these words, then place them in the crossword puzzle to find the hidden message.

	1	U							
2	N								
3						V			
		4	O						
5		N							
	6							E	
7		P							
8		R							
9					I				

After reading

Using what you learned to express your own ideas

5 Give at least two reasons to explain why you agree or disagree with Chris, Don, Mario or Yves. You can use some of the words from the crossword puzzle.

_____

_____

_____

_____

_____

THRILLS, CHILLS
AND HOT BUTTERED POPCORN

Before reading

> Using the context to guess the meaning of unfamiliar words

1 Look at the words in bold in the text. Using the context to help you, match them to the correct definition.

1. hiding
2. to sweat
3. character
4. frightened
5. nightmares
6. viewer
7. exhilarating

a) a person in a movie or in a book
b) bad dreams
c) a person who watches
d) exciting, thrilling
e) trying not to be seen
f) afraid, scared, terrified
g) to become wet because of being hot, nervous or anxious

While reading

> Looking for specific information

2 Answer the following questions as you read the text carefully.

1. What kind of movie does this text talk about?

_____

_____

2. To what does the author compare this kind of movie?

_____

_____

3. What words does the author use to describe the feeling you get when watching this kind of movie?

_____

_____

READING

Thrills, Chills...

Thrills, Chills
and Hot Buttered Popcorn

It's Friday the thirteenth. A group of friends are at a party when the lights suddenly go out. Tom, the school jock, goes down to the basement to check out the fuse box. You feel nervous. You don't like the idea of Tom going down to the basement alone. Someone at the party makes a joke about a maniac **hiding** in the basement. Your heart beats faster and your hands begin **to sweat.** "Don't go," you shout. But Tom can't hear you. Tom is a **character** in a horror movie, and you are among the many **frightened** but thrilled spectators watching from the edge of their theatre seats.

Why do so many teenagers enjoy horror films? Some movie experts believe that people love to be scared. They compare watching horror movies to riding a giant roller-coaster or bungee-jumping. It gives you a thrill and a sense of excitement. There is a perception of risk involved. This kind of film offers you an opportunity to confront your worst **nightmares** while staying in control of the situation. You, the **viewer,** know that whatever may happen to the characters in the movie, nothing will happen to you. No human-eating alien can reach you in your seat. Besides, you can always hide behind your coat jacket or walk out of the movie theatre if the scene scares you too much.

The feeling you get from watching a terrifying horror film can be very **exhilarating.** But, like riding a roller-coaster or bungee-jumping off a bridge, it's not for the faint of heart or the weak of stomach.

3 Look at the title of the text and, with the information from activity 2, write the topic of the text.

This text is about: _____

_____

_____

> **Looking for specific information**

4 Which sentence in the text gives the main idea (the topic sentence)? To find it, follow these steps.

- Think of the topic.
- With a pencil, eliminate the sentences that don't mention the topic.
- Circle the sentences that are left.
- Highlight the sentence that gives the best summary of the text.

The topic sentence: _____

_____

_____

After reading

5 Do you enjoy watching horror films? Explain your answer.

_____

_____

_____

_____

_____

_____

_____

_____

_____

_____

READING

Thrills, Chills...

FISHY SEA-
SERPENT STORIES

Before reading

> *Thinking about what you already know about the topic*

Stories of mythical and legendary creatures have been around for centuries. Though most cultures have their share of these tales, the existence of such creatures remains to be proved.

1 Which of the following creatures have you heard or read about?

☐ Yeti   ☐ centaur   ☐ Sasquatch

☐ mermaid   ☐ Big Foot   ☐ unicorn

☐ dragon   ☐ Pegasus   ☐ Medusa

☐ sea serpent ☐ The Minotaur   ☐ The Abominable Snowman

2 Which of these creatures do you think really exist or existed in the past?

---

3 Tales of sea serpents living in deep lakes around the world are still quite popular today. Which of the following sea serpents do you know about?

☐ The Loch Ness Monster of Scotland

☐ Champ, the sea serpent of Lake Champlain

☐ Memphré, the sea serpent of Lake Memphrémagog, Qué.

☐ Ogopogo in Lake Okanagan, B.C.

☐ The creature of Lake Storsjon, Sweden

☐ The Lake Van monster in Turkey

While reading

> *Looking up the definitions of unfamiliar words*

4 Work with a classmate. One of you works with Text A while the other works with Text B. As you read, underline the words that are unfamiliar or new to you. Choose three of these words and look them up in a dictionary. Keep the context in mind as you select the best definition, and write it in the space provided.

Text: _____

WORD	DEFINITION
1. _____	_____
	_____
2. _____	_____
	_____
3. _____	_____
	_____

5 Explain the words you looked up to your partner. Then read the other text.

A) Excuse Me. Is That a Monster in the Lake?

Throughout the centuries, people have reported seeing strange creatures — known as sea serpents — swimming around the waters of the world. No creature, though, is as intriguing or as famous as the monster from Loch Ness. As early as the sixth century, the people living around Loch Ness, a lake in Scotland, claim to have seen a dinosaur-like monster splashing about the water. This creature, commonly known as The Loch Ness Monster, or Nessie for short, is approximately 12 metres long. Nessie is described as having a huge body with a snake-like tail. It has a long neck like a giraffe, and a head that resembles that of a sheep. Some people who believe they have seen the monster say it has short legs, and that it occasionally walks on the shore. Nessie's skin is said to be smooth, but the colour varies from sighting to sighting, going from grey to dark brown. Though many people say they have seen Nessie, there is no clear evidence that such a creature exists. Many people have taken photos of what they thought was the creature, but these pictures are unclear and offer no proof of the existence of such an incredible animal.

B) Now That's a Big Fish!

In Lake Okanagan, British Columbia, lives a creature called Ogopogo; at least that's what the people who live around the lake say. Some who have seen Ogopogo describe it as a long, snake-like creature with the tail of a whale and the head of a sheep. Eyewitnesses estimate that the monster measures between ten and twelve metres. It has smooth, dark green skin with a yellow and brown design on its back. Unlike its Scottish cousin, the Loch Ness Monster, Ogopogo does not seem to be alone in the lake. There have been reports of up to five Ogopogos swimming around fishing boats at the same time. Despite the many Ogopogo stories, there are no pictures to prove that such a creature really does live in the waters of Lake Okanagan. Nonetheless, firm believers continue searching the lake for evidence of this unusual sea serpent. They hope to show that Ogopogo is more than just a rumour created to attract tourists to the beautiful Okanagan valley.

Fishy Sea-Serpent Stories

6 Go back to the two texts and highlight the information that describes these sea serpents.

7 Decide whether the information given in the two texts is similar or different. Explain your answers. Follow the example.

	SIMILAR	DIFFERENT	REASON
Location of the sea serpents	X	☐	Both are in lakes.
Length of the creatures	☐	☐	
Description of their:			
• heads	☐	☐	
• tails	☐	☐	
• skin texture	☐	☐	
• skin colour	☐	☐	
General description	☐	☐	

8 Find two other differences between Nessie and Ogopogo.

After reading

9 Make up a legend about a sea serpent living in the waters near your town. Give your sea serpent a name. Use the information from the two texts to guide you.

_____

_____

_____

_____

_____

_____

_____

_____

_____

_____

_____

_____

_____

_____

_____

_____

_____

READING

Fishy Sea-Serpent Stories

BREAK-UP
CRISIS

Before reading

Skimming a text

1 First, skim the text on page 70 by reading:
- the introduction
- the first sentence of each paragraph in both letters
- the last paragraph in both letters.

Now look at the introduction again and underline the reason why Scott and Ginger wrote to magazines. Then use your own words to write what you think the two advice letters will say.

_____

_____

_____

2 Underline the first sentence of each paragraph. Use your own words to explain what it says.

LETTER NO. 1

First paragraph: _____

_____

_____

Second paragraph: _____

_____

Third paragraph: _____

_____

LETTER NO. 2

First paragraph: _____

_____

Second paragraph: _____

_____

Third paragraph: _____

_____

While reading

Stopping after each paragraph to think about what you're reading

3 Read both letters and the following statements. For each statement, indicate whether the idea it presents appears in the letters. Follow the example.

STATEMENTS	LETTER NO. 1	LETTER NO. 2
1. Break-ups are painful.	yes	yes
2. Recovery takes time.		
3. Break-ups can teach you how to deal with other negative experiences.		
4. You can learn from a break-up.		
5. Exercise can help you.		
6. Do the things you enjoy doing.		
7. Your friends can help.		
8. Make a list of both the pros and cons of your ex.		
9. Realize that things were not perfect between the two of you.		
10. When all else fails, use magic.		

Break-Up Crisis

Break-Up Crisis

INTRODUCTION

Teens can write to their favourite magazines for advice on how to solve some of their problems. Scott and Ginger sent letters to two different columnists because they wanted to know how they could get over a break-up. Here are the answers that appeared in the magazines the following month.

LETTER NO. 1

Dear S.,

Break-ups are painful, and there's no fixed time frame for how long it takes to get over being dumped. So give yourself plenty of time to mourn the emptiness you feel. One way to get through a break-up is to look at it as an experience that can make you grow stronger and prepare you to deal with all kinds of future disappointments. Tell yourself your life will get better and your broken heart will slowly mend.

Keep in mind that a rich life makes the break-up less crushing and that physical activities can help you get over your "ex." Make a list of all those things you've wanted to do and start doing them. Investing in yourself will make you feel good about who you are and help you regain your self-esteem. So go for it, and flex those muscles.

You could also put away your rose-coloured glasses and make a list of her bad habits. Isolating all of her bad traits and accentuating the negative aspects of your relationship could make you see that you deserve better than what she could give you.

LETTER NO. 2

Dear G.,

Breaking up is really hard, especially if it happens unexpectedly. It's hard to let go of someone you've loved, and you might feel angry and hurt. Getting over someone can take some time, and feelings aren't faucets that can just be turned off. Break-ups can teach you how to take an objective look at what you want from a relationship and realize how much you've learned and gained from this experience.

For now, what's important is to get back to your friends and hobbies and regain your independence. So boost yourself up by doing anything that you enjoy and that will make you feel good again.

If, after doing this, you're still not over him, you could make a list of what you liked and what you didn't like about him. You might find that the bad list is longer than the good one — that will be a big wake-up call for you! Who knows? After taking this inventory you might even feel like...

After reading

4 Imagine that you are the advice columnist for a teen magazine. What advice would you give to someone who was having trouble dealing with a break-up? Write an ending for Letter No. 2 by continuing the final sentence.

Who knows? After taking this inventory you might even feel like...

_____

_____

_____

_____

_____

_____

_____

_____

_____

_____

_____

_____

_____

READING

Break-Up Crisis

ALL
AROUND US

Before reading

> *Thinking about what you already know about the topic*

1 Place the words from the environmental word bank under the heading they seem to be most closely related to. Some of the words can go into more than one category.

ENVIRONMENTAL WORD BANK

recycling	pollution	acid rain	tree-planting
pesticides	landfills (dumps)	incinerators	deforestation
animal habitat	ozone layer	global warming	greenhouse effect

GARBAGE _____

AIR _____

WATER _____

FORESTS _____

While reading

> *Focusing on key words to understand a text*

2 Read the four introductions and the six possible conclusions starting on page 73. Find the conclusion that gives the best solution to the problem raised in each introduction.

Introduction 1: Conclusion _____

Introduction 3: Conclusion _____

Introduction 2: Conclusion _____

Introduction 4: Conclusion _____

3 Match each definition with the correct environmental term.

1. waste that can be used to enrich the soil ☐   **a)** extinction

2. wise use of natural resources ☐   **b)** global warming

3. cutting down of trees ☐   **c)** compost

4. the natural home of an animal or plant ☐   **d)** erosion

5. the disappearance of a species from the earth ☐   **e)** reusing

6. the increase of the earth's temperature ☐   **f)** habitat

7. land made from garbage ☐   **g)** ecosystem

8. using something more than once ☐   **h)** conservation

9. the washing away of topsoil ☐   **i)** deforestation

10. a community of living things and its environment ☐   **j)** landfill

All Around Us

INTRODUCTION ONE

Most of the things we throw away, including old clothes, furniture and appliances, end up in landfills or dumps. In these out-of-the-way places, often on low-lying lands, bulldozers spread the garbage and pack it down. Even so, landfills take up a lot of space.

INTRODUCTION TWO

The contamination of the air causes problems like acid rain, global warming and the destruction of the ozone layer. The major sources of pollution are trucks and buses, incinerators and factories.

READING

All Around Us

INTRODUCTION THREE

Water pollution is threatening our water supply. Some major pollutants include sewage, chemicals from factories and fertilizers, as well as weed and bug killers. Another major threat is the overuse of water, which could lead to our not having enough water left to survive.

INTRODUCTION FOUR

People often have good reasons to cut down trees: we need space and lumber to build houses and other buildings, and we need paper. Unfortunately, though, deforestation destroys animal habitats, causes erosion and affects our whole ecosystem.

CONCLUSION A

...companies are looking for more efficient ways to dispose of their waste, and farmers are trying to grow crops without using fertilizers or insecticides. In every sector, people are trying to use this natural resource more wisely.

CONCLUSION B

...keeping a compost pile for our vegetable peels and reusing things instead of throwing them away, we reduce the amount of garbage and provide material for making other products.

CONCLUSION C

...is being reduced in some areas. Some lakes are being cleaned up and a lot of effort is going into restoring the plant and fish life that were threatened with extinction.

CONCLUSION D

...some of these gases keep the earth warm so we can live here. The larger amounts that are produced by factories and cars may hold too much heat and cause global warming.

CONCLUSION E

...are being planted faster than they are cut down. More and more people are also helping the conservation process by recycling paper.

CONCLUSION F

...cars burn less gasoline. More and more power plants and factories use special devices to remove harmful chemicals before they come out of the smokestacks and enter the air.

Relating the information in the text to what you already know about the topic

4 Choose one of the introductions and add two or three sentences to link it to its conclusion.

Example: People often have good reasons to cut down trees: we need space and lumber to build houses and other buildings, and we need paper. Unfortunately, though, deforestation destroys animal habitats, causes erosion and affects our whole ecosystem. *It is also the cause of plant and animal extinction. For example, more than a thousand species of birds are in danger of becoming extinct. This is why so many people consider the survival of our beautiful forests as a priority, and why so many trees* are being planted faster than they are cut down. More and more people are also helping the conservation process by recycling paper.

_____

_____

_____

_____

_____

_____

_____

_____

_____

_____

_____

_____

_____

_____

_____

_____

READING

All Around Us

WHEN AN IRONMAN
IS A WOMAN

Before reading

> Relating the topic of a text to yourself

1 Try to answer these questions. They will help you understand how difficult the Ironman Hawaiian Championship really is.

1. What town could you get to if you biked 179 km from school?

_____

2. Where could you be if you ran 41.9 km from home?

_____

3. How many Olympic pool lengths would you have to swim to cover 3.8 km?

_____

> Using titles, subtitles and captions to get the general idea of a text

2 Read the title, subtitles and captions. Write what you think the text is about.

_____
_____
_____
_____

While reading

> Looking for specific information

3 Read the text and answer the questions.

1. Is the Ironman Triathlon World Championship a popular event? Give evidence to support your answer. _____

_____

2. Describe the three events in the Hawaiian Ironman Triathlon. _____

_____

3. How long does it take to complete the triathlon in Hawaii? _____

4. How long had Isabelle Gagnon been training when she participated in the Hawaiian Ironman? _____

5. Describe her weekly schedule. _____

_____

When an Ironman is a Woman

Every year, millions of television viewers worldwide have their eyes glued to the Ironman Triathlon World Championship held in Kailua-Kona, Hawaii. More than 20 000 triathletes enter 22 national and international qualifying events, but only 1500 win the chance to compete in this most prestigious triathlon of the year. In 1997, twenty-three-year-old Isabelle Gagnon from Charlesbourg, Quebec, a Canadian champion several times over, was among the 271 women competitors.

Why is this event so special?
The Ironman in Hawaii is a long-course or ultra-distance triathlon. It features a 3.8-km swim in the Pacific Ocean, a 179-km bicycle race and a 41.9-km marathon. Top competitors take from 8 to 9 hours to finish the event, and all contestants must complete the race within 17 hours. The average time is about 12 hours; Isabelle took only 10 hours and 15 minutes to reach the finish line. This excellent performance earned her an eighth-place finish among the women, and first place in both the amateur category and her age group. Her coach and all of her fans in Charlesbourg are extremely proud that she was talented enough to perform so well in a competition triathletes consider "the ultimate test" after only three years of training.

Working steadily and enjoying the rugged beauty of the lava-formed valleys and cliffs on the Big Island of Hawaii.

Twenty-three-year-old Isabelle Gagnon completing the Ironman — the ultimate endurance challenge.

Finishing the 3.8-km swim in the Pacific Ocean.

Who can become a triathlete?

Triathletes must be very determined and train rigorously if they want to attain their goals. Isabelle admits that you also have to be a little crazy to put yourself through such an ordeal. Just look at her training schedule:

	Mon	Tue	Wed	Thu	Fri	Sat	Sun	Total Hours
Swim	X		X		X	X		4
Bike		X		X				7
Run	X	X	X	X	X	X		6

A typical week includes 10 km of swimming, 360 km of biking and 70 km of running, not to mention a few hours of weight training. To complete this weekly marathon, Isabelle has a part-time job and is studying at Laval University for her Master's degree.

Is it worth all the effort?

Isabelle has a multitude of reasons for training and competing, but most important to her is the amazing sense of accomplishment she gets from working so hard. Pushing herself both physically and mentally to reach her goals appeals to her. "If I can do this," Isabelle says, "I can do anything."

After reading

4 Write five questions you would like to ask Isabelle or another triathlete.

1. _____

   _____

   _____

2. _____

   _____

   _____

3. _____

   _____

   _____

4. _____

   _____

   _____

5. _____

   _____

   _____

READING

When an Ironman is a Woman

OPERATION
NOAH

Before reading

> *Thinking about what you already know about the topic*

1 What do you know about the tale of Noah's Ark? Discuss it with your classmates. Then, on your own, write a few sentences that summarize this tale.

_____

_____

_____

_____

> *Using the title, illustrations and captions to get the general idea of a text*

2 Look at the title of the text on page 81 and read the caption under the illustration. What do you think this story will be about?

_____

_____

While reading

> *Using the context to guess the meaning of unfamiliar words*

3 Read the text *Operation Noah*. Find the words that have the same meaning as:

1. people who study a lot in a special field, learned people

_____

2. barrier blocking the passage of water

_____

3. the overflowing water from a lake or a river

_____

4. left in a helpless position

_____

5. an official responsible for supervising and protecting animals

_____

READING

Operation Noah

6. mammals, birds and fish that are not domesticated

_____

7. save

_____

8. flat structures used for transportation on water

_____

9. assemble into a pack and move together

_____

10. tranquillized

_____

Operation Noah

A popular tale found in different religions is the story of a great flood, and how a man named Noah rescued the animals of the world from this disaster. Noah built a ship called an ark, and filled it with two animals of each species. After forty days of rain, the ark landed on a mountain top, and the animal kingdom was saved. Scientists and religious scholars are still trying to discover whether this tale is fact or fiction.

There is another story, this one definitely true, that deals with a modern-day Noah and how he saved the animals of the Zambezi Valley, in Africa. His name is Rupert Fothergill, and this is his tale.

This rhino can finally float to safety, thanks to the hard work and perseverance of Fothergill and his team of conservationists.

When the government of Rhodesia (today's Zambia and Zimbabwe) built a dam to harness the waters of the Zambezi River, it created the largest man-made lake in the world, Lake Kariba. The dam was developed to supply hydroelectricity to Central Africa. The project had its share of problems, including two disastrous floods.

(continued)

Operation Noah

Thousands of people who lived along the Zambezi River were moved to other locations. The animals, however, were not. Eventually, as the valley became flooded, the animals were left stranded on tiny islands throughout the lake. Rupert Fothergill, a conservationist and game warden, set up a wildlife rescue mission called Operation Noah. The people involved in the rescue mission set out in boats and rafts to try to save the animals. It wasn't an easy task.

The animals had to be trapped first. In order to move them safely to a new environment, the wardens had to herd the animals and force them to swim across the lake. Some animals, such as the rhinoceros, could not swim. They had to be sedated with special darts and then loaded onto rafts. It took several hours just to catch one rhino—and there were thousands of animals to save. Among the animals that had to be rescued was the dangerous black mamba, a poisonous snake found in that area. One ranger climbed a tree in order to catch one of the mambas that was stuck there. The people involved in Operation Noah set aside their own safety to save the wildlife that would have died without their aid.

The operation lasted many months. Over 6 000 animals, including elephants, lions, baboons, zebras and snakes, were brought to safer grounds. The animals were relocated to the mountainous Matusadona region and are doing quite well today, thanks to Rupert Fothergill and Operation Noah.

> Scanning a text to find specific information

4 Look at the following questions and find the answers in the text.

1. Where does this story take place? _____

_____

2. Who was responsible for the rescue mission? _____

_____

3. How did they save the different animals? _____

_____

4. What were some of the difficulties of the rescue mission? _____

_____

After reading

> *Using what you learned to express your own ideas*

5 How does this rescue mission compare with the tale of Noah's Ark? List some of the similarities and some of the differences.

SIMILARITIES:

_____

_____

_____

_____

_____

_____

_____

_____

DIFFERENCES:

_____

_____

_____

_____

_____

_____

_____

_____

_____

CRYOPRESERVATION:
THE PROSPECT OF IMMORTALITY

More than sixty known patients who could not be kept alive by the medical knowledge and technology of our era have chosen to be preserved at low temperatures for future treatment. These people have paid up to $140 000 to be put in suspension, without knowing whether doctors will ever find a cure for the illness that caused their death. In this text, six people give their opinions on the delicate matter of the process known as cryonics.

Before reading

> Scanning a text to find specific information

1 Move your eyes quickly through the text to find the following information. Highlight your answers.

1. Scan for the word **cryonics** and its derivatives.
2. Scan to find a synonym for the word **moral,** then for a word that means its opposite.
3. Scan for words related to medicine.

While reading

> Focusing on key words to find specific information

2 Read the text carefully and answer the questions.

1. Which section is not specifically about cryonics?

   Opinion _____

2. Which two sections mention the moral implications of cryonics?

   Opinions _____ and _____

3. Which two sections mention the responsibility that future generations must take for cryonics patients?

   Opinions _____ and _____

4. Which two sections are about the resistance of the medical world toward cryonics?

   Opinions _____ and _____

3 Find five arguments *against* cryopreservation.

1. _____

   _____

2. _____

   _____

3. _____

   _____

4. _____

   _____

5. _____

   _____

Cryopreservation:
The Prospect of Immortality

Opinion A: I'm sure there are many good reasons for choosing cryopreservation over the traditional after-death routes. But I find this way of preserving our bodies quite morbid. Anyway, life is hard enough one time around, so why would anyone want to come back for another?

Opinion B: Historically, the idea of reviving people is quite old. According to fifteenth-century Italian literature, midwives used mouth-to-mouth breathing techniques to resuscitate newborn babies. In the sixteenth century, physicians learned that this simple technique could also work on adults and that it was possible to save some of them from death.

Opinion C: These far-from-innocent cryonic suspension experiments involve both social and ethical considerations. If we knew about the dangers of such projects, we could find ways to protect ourselves. What will happen when these twentieth-century people are brought back? Will they be able to take care of themselves or will someone else have to do it? Will they adapt to the new society or will they be helpless and miserable? And what if they carry germs that people are no longer immune to because those diseases have been wiped out?

Opinion D: When we examine the history of medicine, we can see that almost no important new idea has been easily accepted. In our present social context, cryonic freezing is considered by most people to be immoral. This delicate matter requires serious consideration. In any case, the medical field won't accept cryonics until our culture is ready for it.

Opinion E: A number of advances in research are required before we can even think of reviving people in cryonic suspension. Fortunately, for the moment, scientists only have to know how to put the patients into suspension; the procedure that will be used to revive them is left for future cryobiologists to explore.

(continued)

Opinion F: A lot of medical discoveries were made by people who were not doctors. Pasteur, for example, was a chemist. Fleming was a bacteriologist and midwives shared their method of mouth-to-mouth resuscitation with doctors. It's no secret that some medical fields seem more reluctant than others to accept new ideas. We can only wonder how many lives might have been saved if the field of medicine had been quicker to accept scientific discoveries. Let's hope they won't ignore cryonics for too long.

After reading

> Thinking about what you learned about the topic

4 Use your own words to explain what cryopreservation is.

_____

_____

_____

_____

> Using the information from the text to express an opinion

5 Would you consider cryopreservation if you or someone you loved had a fatal illness? Explain your answer.

_____

_____

_____

_____

_____

_____

_____

_____

_____

_____

_____

_____

_____

_____

_____

_____

READING

Cryopreservation...

KNITTING
WITH STEEL

Before reading

> Skimming a text to find information

1 Look at the title and illustrations that accompany the text. What do you think this text is about?

My prediction: _____

2 Highlight the first and last paragraphs of *Knitting with Steel*. Then, highlight the first sentence of each of the other paragraphs. Read only what you have highlighted to answer the following questions.

1. Who is this story about? _____

_____

_____

2. What do they do? _____

_____

3. How do you think they learned about this activity? _____

_____

4. Why do they do this activity? _____

_____

_____

5. Which of the following statements is true?

   a) I will read about knitting. ☐

   b) I will read about the history of coats of mail. ☐

   c) I will read steps to make a coat of mail. ☐

   d) I will read how to play medieval games. ☐

3 Does the information you found support or contradict the prediction you made in number 1?

_____

_____

_____

While reading

4 Read the text *Knitting with Steel* completely to verify your prediction and to learn more about this interesting hobby. As you read, complete Figures 1, 2 and 3 by placing the following words in their proper places.

wire	rod	coil	links	pliers	cutters

Knitting with Steel

Eric, David and Bruno are just your average high school seniors, with one exception. They like **to knit** in their spare time. You can see them almost every noon in the school cafeteria plying their trade.[1] Armed with cutters and pliers, these boys labour diligently on their works of art. What does knitting have to do with these tools? Everything, when the object you are making is a coat of mail.

One day the boys, long-time fans of medieval role-playing games, were searching the Internet for any information on the Middle Ages. They came upon a web site that explained how to make chain-mail patterns. And the rest, as they say, is history.

To create one of these coats, they need wire, wire cutters, pliers and a lot of cooperation. Bruno, who is a self-proclaimed jack-of-all-trades,[2] starts off the procedure by **winding** wire onto a rod (Fig. 1). He wraps the steel wire into a coil that looks like a spring. He then passes the coil to David, who cuts it into circles called links (Fig. 2). This step is hard on the hands and David has the calluses[3] to prove it. Eric does the actual knitting or assembling of the coat. He joins the links together using pliers. There are many **patterns** to follow, but the one the boys prefer is called a 4-in-1 European pattern. This means they join four links together with one common link in the middle (Fig. 3). Bruno also helps with the cutting and assembling once his winding job is done.

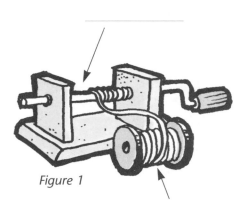

Figure 1

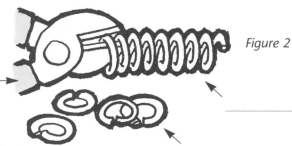

Figure 2

1. *plying their trade: working industriously at*
2. *jack-of-all-trades: a person who does many different tasks*
3. *callus: a thickening or hardening of the skin*

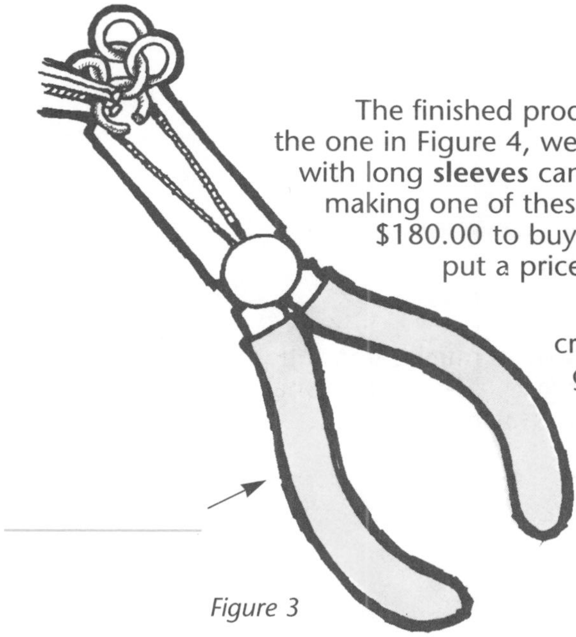

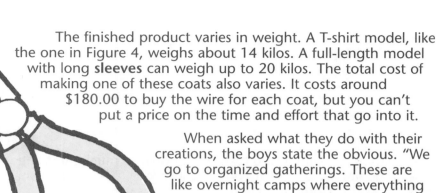

The finished product varies in weight. A T-shirt model, like the one in Figure 4, weighs about 14 kilos. A full-length model with long **sleeves** can weigh up to 20 kilos. The total cost of making one of these coats also varies. It costs around $180.00 to buy the wire for each coat, but you can't put a price on the time and effort that go into it.

When asked what they do with their creations, the boys state the obvious. "We go to organized gatherings. These are like overnight camps where everything is decorated in medieval style. We can fight battles or monsters using foam **weapons**. It's a lot of fun, and you get to see some really nice costumes. And some day," Bruno adds with a smile, "we hope to sell them."

Figure 3

Figure 4

Using the context to guess the meaning of unfamiliar words

5 Match each word to its definition. The words appear in bold in the text.

1. to knit	☐	**a)** models or examples, designs
2. winding	☐	**b)** to join together, to link
3. patterns	☐	**c)** instrument used in combat
4. sleeves	☐	**d)** a turning movement
5. weapons	☐	**e)** part of clothing that covers the arms

Scanning for specific information

6 Look at the questions below. Read the text again and underline the information you want. Write down your answers.

a) What tools do you need to make a coat of mail? _____

b) What are the three steps to making a coat of mail?

  1. _____

  2. _____

  3. _____

c) How much does a coat of mail weigh? _____

Knitting with Steel

After reading

7 Without looking at the text, write down as much information as you can remember about what you have just read. Use an extra sheet of paper if necessary. Compare your notes with a classmate's.

_____

_____

_____

_____

_____

_____

_____

Using what you learned to express your own ideas

8 Would this hobby interest you? Explain your answer.

_____

_____

_____

_____

_____

_____

_____

_____

_____

READING

Knitting with Steel

# STEREOTYPES,
OR JUDGING A BOOK BY ITS COVER

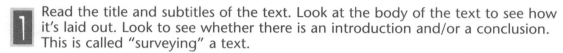# Before reading

> *Surveying a text*

1 Read the title and subtitles of the text. Look at the body of the text to see how it's laid out. Look to see whether there is an introduction and/or a conclusion. This is called "surveying" a text.

Now circle the letter that corresponds to the best answer to each of the following questions:

1. What is this text about?

a) people who are stereotyped
b) stereotyping and society
c) the definition, causes and effects of stereotyping

2. Which of the following ideas will probably not be in this text?

a) why stereotyping is popular among teens
b) the negative impact of stereotyping on individuals
c) the social consequences of stereotyping

2 Use your own words to explain the title of the text.

_____

_____

_____

# While reading

> *Focusing on key words to find specific information*

3
a) Read the sentences that follow. Identify and underline the key words. The first few sentences have been done for you.

b) Read the text carefully. Write the **first three words** of a sentence in the text that is similar in meaning to each of the following sentences. There may be several possible answers. Be prepared to explain your choice.

READING

Stereotypes...

1. Stereotyping <u>doesn't take</u> the <u>complete personality</u> of an individual into <u>account</u>.

   _____

2. Stereotyping is like <u>judging</u> people because of the <u>colour</u> of their <u>skin</u> or their <u>gender</u>.

   _____

3. Some <u>people</u> are <u>categorized</u> because of the <u>way they look</u>.

   _____

4. People who are stereotyped sometimes modify their behaviour according to what is expected of them.

   _____

5. What's frustrating is that people who stereotype don't even take the time to get to know you.

   _____

6. Every one of us is unique.

   _____

7. As members of society, we all benefit from working together.

   _____

Stereotypes, or Judging a Book by Its Cover

What is stereotyping?
Stereotyping is taking your own general impression about a particular type of person and applying it to all individuals of that type. When people make comments like "all blondes are dumb" or "all long-haired teens are junkies," they are using stereotypes. Stereotypes acknowledge only one dimension of who a person is.

Why do people stereotype others?
Lumping a group of people into the same category doesn't take much time, thought or energy. Those who are quick to label others may simply find it easier to pass judgment than to make the effort to relate to people they see as different from themselves. Because of this, they tend to miss out on getting to know the individuals they are stereotyping.

Is stereotyping a problem?
Some people consider stereotyping to be a form of prejudice, just like racism and sexism. Labelling people based on how they dress or cut their hair, or on what music they like, doesn't take into account any of the variations that make individuals unique. But is that really such a big problem?

There are those who believe that stereotyping can destroy a person's self-esteem. They even say that if it lasts long enough, people can actually come to believe what is said about them and start behaving in a way that conforms to the stereotype. Let's look at a couple of examples. Read Andy's and Lainy's stories about their high school years:

Stereotypes...

Andy's story: I was really athletic in high school, and maybe not at the top of my class. A few people started calling me a "dumb jock," and it really caught on. Eventually, I really did start to fail my exams. I was convinced that I was nothing more than what other people said I was.

Lainy's story: I was a great student, but I wore glasses and didn't dress in cool clothes. It didn't take long before the other kids at school started calling me "Brainy Lainy." Only my closest friends in the neighbourhood knew that I was also a really good soccer player. You know, I was proud of my grades, but I was always frustrated that so many of my classmates thought that studying was the only thing I was good at.

Should stereotyping have a place in our society?

Though we may share certain affinities with some people, let's face it: no two of us are exactly alike. This fact has allowed us to evolve as a society. Just think — the first person who thought of using fire to cook food must have seemed pretty unique to others, but if that individual had not been so special, what would you be eating for dinner tonight? Considering that society is the culmination of individual efforts working cooperatively for the improvement of human life, one has to wonder if there is room for stereotyping in our world. Remembering that each person is a unique combination of characteristics and abilities will help us to get past the stereotypes and see each other for the multi-dimensional people we really are. Now doesn't that sound more interesting?

After reading

> *Using what you learned to express your own ideas*

4 Do you agree with what the text says about stereotyping? Write your opinion and give two examples of your own to support your point of view.

_____

_____

_____

_____

_____

_____

_____

_____

_____

_____

_____

_____

_____

READING

Stereotypes...

More Tips, Tricks and Strategies
to Help Me Become a Better Reader

PRODUCTION ACTIVITIES

STRATEGIES FOR WRITING

Before writing

Plan what you want to write by. . .

Asking yourself questions about the topic
Brainstorming for ideas
Brainstorming the vocabulary you will need
Making an outline to organize the information you want to write about
Mapping out your ideas
Thinking about your audience (reader) and the purpose of your text
Writing notes

While writing

Write a draft by. . .

Free-writing without thinking about spelling or grammar
Modifying your outline if necessary
Referring to your outline and your notes often
Respecting the guidelines for the type of text you are writing
    (letter of opinion, story, letter of intent, etc.)

After writing

Edit your draft by. . .

Checking the instructions carefully
Checking your grammar, spelling and sentence structure
Having a classmate organize or map the information you are writing about
Having a classmate proofread your text for clarity, spelling and grammar
Having a classmate make an outline of your text
Making sure your story line or ideas are organized logically

STRATEGIES FOR SPEAKING

Before speaking

Plan what you want to say by. . .

Asking yourself questions about the topic
Brainstorming the vocabulary you will need
Brainstorming for ideas

P-1 THE SIMPLE PRESENT

GRAMMAR

The simple present tense is used to talk about habits. It is also used to express a general truth or fact, likes, dislikes and wants. Finally, we can use it to express a feeling, perception or state that's happening right now.

THE VERB TO BE		OTHER VERBS	
Affirmative	Negative	Affirmative	Negative
I am happy.	I'm not happy.	I play hockey.	I don't play hockey.
You are sure.	You're not sure.	You sing well.	You don't sing well.
He is popular. She is popular. It is popular.	He's not popular. She's not popular. It's not popular.	He eats corn. She eats corn. It eats corn.	He doesn't eat corn. She doesn't eat corn. It doesn't eat corn.
We are late.	We're not late.	We study hard.	We don't study hard.
They are surprised.	They're not surprised.	They like art.	They don't like art.

THE VERB TO HAVE	
Affirmative	Negative
I have a cute dog.	I don't have a cute dog.
You have beautiful eyes.	You don't have beautiful eyes.
He/She/It has good teeth.	He/She/It doesn't have good teeth.
We have a good team.	We don't have a good team.
They have twins.	They don't have twins.

> *Here are some key words that are often used with the simple present tense:*
>
> ***every day/week/month/Tuesday/year/etc.*** • ***usually*** • ***always*** • ***often*** ***sometimes*** • ***never***

Practice

1 Circle the subject and any key words in each sentence. Write the simple present tense of the verb in parentheses and indicate what it expresses.

USED TO EXPRESS...

1. (I) _am_ (to be) 16 years old (today). _a fact_
2. We _____ (to eat) breakfast at 7:30. _____
3. Every day, school _____ (to start) at 9 o'clock. _____
4. Lucy _____ (to want) to play in a band. _____
5. I _____ (to like) to watch TV every evening. _____
6. Janine and Abdul always _____ (to have) lunch at that restaurant. _____
7. I _____ (to smell) rotten fish. _____
8. Charles really _____ (to hate) my girlfriend. _____
9. We _____ (to need) water to survive. _____
10. She often _____ (to have) mood swings. _____

2 Now write five of the sentences above in the negative form.

Example: *I am not 16 years old today.*

1. _____
2. _____
3. _____
4. _____
5. _____

ASKING QUESTIONS WITH THE VERB TO BE IN THE SIMPLE PRESENT TENSE

YES/NO QUESTIONS			INFORMATION QUESTIONS			
Verb (V)	Subject (S)	The Rest of the Question (ROQ)	Question Word (QW)	V	S	ROQ
Am	I	good-looking?	Where	am	I?	
Are	you	sure?	How	are	you?	
Is	he/she/it	outside?	Who	is		outside?
Are	we	partners?	Why	are	we	here?
Are	they	brothers?	What	are	they?	

ASKING QUESTIONS WITH OTHER VERBS

Information Questions QW	Yes/No Questions Auxiliary (Aux.)	S	V	ROQ
	Do	you	have	any money?
Where	does	Helen	live?	
When	do	we	leave?	
	Do	they	play	basketball?

When the information we are looking for is the subject of the sentence, we use a slightly different word order:

QW	V	ROQ	Answer
Who	lives	here?	The Jacksons.
Which animal	has	long legs?	The giraffe.

Practice

3 Unscramble the yes/no questions and the information questions and write them in the chart below. Don't forget to place a question mark at the end of each question.

1. with Billy / who / that person / is
2. for breakfast / does / he / what / eat
3. Cathy and Jessie / where / live / do / now
4. is / when / lunch
5. they / always here / are / why
6. soup / is / how / your
7. a famous actor / you / are
8. Josh / your boyfriend / is
9. a lot of money / she / spend / does
10. Mr. and Mrs. Jones / do / every summer / travel

	QW	Aux. or To Be	S	V	ROQ
1.					
2.					
3.					
4.					
5.					
6.					
7.					
8.					
9.					
10.					

4 Use the simple present tense of the verbs in parentheses to complete this e-mail letter.

```
┌──────────────────────────────────────────────────────────────────┐
│ □ ▒▒▒▒▒▒▒▒▒▒▒▒▒▒ Message Composition ▒▒▒▒▒▒▒▒▒▒▒▒▒▒▒ 回 目         │
├──────────────────────────────────────────────────────────────────┤
│ ┌─────┐ ┌─────┐ ┌─────┐ ┌─────┐  ┌─────┐                          │
│ │ ✉  │ │ 📋 │ │ ✎  │ │ 🖨 │  │ ● │  From: Hill@Charlesbourg.Qc.ca │
│ │SendNow│ Quote │ Attach│Address│  │ Stop │                        │
│ └─────┘ └─────┘ └─────┘ └─────┘  └─────┘                          │
│                                                                    │
│ Subject: ┌──────────────────────────────────────────┐             │
│          │ Looking for an e-mail correspondent      │             │
│          └──────────────────────────────────────────┘             │
│ ▷ Addressing                          Attachments                  │
│ ┌───────────────────────────────────┐▲ ┌─────────────────────┐▲   │
│ │ Mail To: Newfriends@Scotland      │  │                     │     │
│ │    Cc:                            │  │                     │     │
│ │                                   │▼ │                     │▼   │
│ └───────────────────────────────────┘  └─────────────────────┘    │
│ ┌───────────────────────────────────────────────────────────┐▲   │
│ │ Date: October 10                                          │     │
│ │                                                           │     │
│ │ Dear Ian,                                                 │     │
│ │                                                           │     │
│ │ My name is Andrea Hill and I would like to correspond     │     │
│ │ with teenagers from Scotland on the Internet. I           │     │
│ │ _____ (be) sixteen years old, and I _____ │     │
│ │ (have) brown hair and blue eyes. My family and I          │     │
│ │ _____ (live) in Charlesbourg, but we usually      │     │
│ │ _____ (spend) the summer in the Maritimes with    │     │
│ │ my grandparents. I _____ (be) very active and I   │     │
│ │ _____ (enjoy) outdoor activities like cycling     │     │
│ │ and snowboarding. Both my parents _____ (work).   │     │
│ │ My younger brother Benjamin _____│     │
│ │ _____ (go, negative) to school yet.       │     │
│ │                                                           │     │
│ │ I _____ (be) sure that your traditions            │     │
│ │ _____ (be) very different from ours. For          │     │
│ │ example, we always _____ (eat) turkey for         │     │
│ │ Thanksgiving and we _____ (celebrate) Saint-Jean- │     │
│ │ Baptiste and Canada Day with fireworks and bonfires.      │     │
│ │                                                           │     │
│ │ And what about you? What _____ (like,         │     │
│ │ question) to do in your spare time? How _____   │     │
│ │ _____ (celebrate, question) special  │     │
│ │ events in your country? If you _____ (feel) we    │     │
│ │ _____ (have) things in common, please            │     │
│ │ _____ (contact) me at my e-mail address.         │     │
│ │                                                           │     │
│ │ Sincerely,                                                │     │
│ │                                                           │     │
│ │ Andrea                                                    │▼   │
│ └───────────────────────────────────────────────────────────┘    │
│ ◄ ──────────────────────────────────────────────────────── ►     │
└──────────────────────────────────────────────────────────────────┘
```

The Simple Present

PRODUCTION

WRITTEN PRODUCTION

WRITING AN E-MAIL MESSAGE

This assignment consists of writing an e-mail message to a teenager you met on the Internet. Your message could include the following:

- A short description of yourself (age, physical description)
- Your habits, pastimes, likes and dislikes
- An explanation of how you celebrate special occasions with your family and friends (birthdays, holidays, etc.)
- Information about what makes this country special (weather, languages, etc.)

Ask at least three questions about your computer friend's country and lifestyle. Use about 100 words.

Before writing

Decide on the subjects you want to write about. Consider the order of presentation for each subject.

_____

_____

_____

_____

_____

_____

_____

_____

_____

_____

_____

After writing

Once you've written your draft, check the following:

- Are your ideas logically organized?
- Did you use the simple present tense correctly?

Write your final version in the provided e-mail form. Respect the format of an e-mail letter. Write your e-mail address, the receiver's name, the subject of the letter and the date. Finally, end your letter with a form of salutation and write your name.

Message Composition

| Send Now | Quote | Attach | Address | Stop |

From:_____

Subject: [_____]

Addressing

Mail To: _____

Cc: _____

Attachments

Date:_____

Dear_____,

_____

_____

_____

_____

_____

_____

_____

_____

_____

_____

_____

_____

_____

_____

_____

_____

_____

_____

_____

_____

_____

_____

_____

_____

_____

_____

_____

_____

_____

_____

_____

_____,

_____

(signature)

ORAL PRODUCTION

INFORMATION SEARCH

Find out interesting and revealing information about students your own age.

Before speaking

1 Prepare five questions to ask your classmates. Use the simple present tense to express the kind of idea written in the parentheses.

For example, **Q. 1:** (habit): *Do you eat poutine every week?*

Q. 1 (habit): _____

_____

Q. 2 (general truth or fact): _____

_____

Q. 3 (like or dislike): _____

_____

Q. 4 (want): _____

_____

Q. 5 (feeling, perception or state): _____

_____

2 Check the structure of your questions with another student.

While speaking

3 Ask three classmates your questions and write down their answers.

Q. 1 student 1: _____

student 2: _____

student 3: _____

Q. 2 student 1: _____

student 2: _____

student 3: _____

Q. 3 student 1: _____

student 2: _____

student 3: _____

Q. 4 student 1: _____

student 2: _____

student 3: _____

Q. 5 student 1: _____

student 2: _____

student 3: _____

After speaking

4 On a loose-leaf sheet, prepare five graphs to illustrate the answers to your questions.

For example: **Q. 1:** (habit) *"Do you eat poutine every week?"*

yes (2)

no (3)

5 **a)** In teams of four, present your graphs. Compare the questions you prepared and the answers you got.

b) Which questions do you find most interesting or most revealing about students your age?

GRAMMAR

The simple past tense is used to express a completed action or to describe a situation in the past. Regular verbs form the past with **-ed.** The forms of the irregular verbs must be learned. Use the list on page 153 for reference.

▼ ▼

PAST	NOW	FUTURE

I miss**ed** the chair and **fell** on the floor.

Notice that the form is the same for all persons—except in the case of the verb **to be.** Regular and irregular verbs form the negative in the same way.

REGULAR VERBS		IRREGULAR VERBS	
Affirmative	Negative	Affirmative	Negative
I washed.	I didn't wash.	I ate.	I didn't eat.
You washed.	You didn't wash.	You ate.	You didn't eat.
He/She/It washed.	He/She/It didn't wash.	He/She/It ate.	He/She/It didn't eat.
We washed.	We didn't wash.	We ate.	We didn't eat.
They washed.	They didn't wash.	They ate.	They didn't eat.

THE VERB TO BE	
Affirmative	Negative
I was in trouble.	I wasn't in trouble.
You were the cause.	You weren't the cause.
He/She/It was involved.	He/She/It wasn't involved.
We were worried.	We weren't worried.
They were too.	They weren't either

Here are some key words that are often used with the simple past tense:

yesterday • yesterday morning • yesterday afternoon • two weeks ago

in 1992 • last night/week/month/year/etc.

Note the spelling of certain regular verbs:

stop ⟹ stop**ped**   plan ⟹ plan**ned**   try ⟹ tr**ied**   study ⟹ stud**ied**

Practice

1 Look at the following activities. Place a ✓ next to the activities you did last week. Place an **X** next to the ones you didn't do.

- ☐ Jump out of a plane
- ☐ Watch television
- ☐ Shop for new clothes
- ☐ Buy a new CD
- ☐ Play a game
- ☐ Run in a marathon
- ☐ Take the bus to school
- ☐ Walk to school
- ☐ Drive to school
- ☐ Go to a party
- ☐ Sleep at your best friend's house
- ☐ Eat at the school cafeteria

Using the information above, write ten sentences telling what you did and didn't do last week. Give details whenever possible.

Example: *Last week, I watched the hockey game on television. I didn't sleep at Jenna's house.*

ASKING QUESTIONS IN THE SIMPLE PAST TENSE

QW	Aux.	S	V	ROQ
	Did	you	buy	the blue jeans with the red shirt?
Why	did	she	stop	the game?
When	did	they	go?	

ASKING QUESTIONS WITH THE VERB TO BE

QW	V	S	ROQ
	Was	there	a test yesterday?
Who	was	that masked man?	
Why	were	you	so nervous?

GRAMMAR

The Simple Past

PRODUCTION

2 Fill in the following dialogue by completing the questions. Observe the answers carefully for clues.

Julia: _____ yesterday?

Tony: I went to a comic book convention.

Julia: _____ alone?

Tony: No, I was with Paul and Terry.

Julia: _____ a lot of people?

Tony: Yes, there were a lot of people. The room was packed.

Julia: _____ ?

Tony: Yes, we had a lot of fun. There were tons of comic books for sale.

Julia: _____ anything?

Tony: Yes, I bought myself a few *Action Joe* comic books.

Julia: _____ ?

Tony: They cost me three dollars total. They complete my collection.

Julia: _____ about the convention?

Tony: Paul told me about it. He saw an ad in a comic book.

Julia: _____ that I collect comic books too?

Tony: No, I didn't know that.

Julia: Next time let me know. I'll go with you.

Tony: Sure, no problem.

3 Complete the text on a personal hero. Use the simple past tense.

A Personal Hero

Terry Fox is my personal hero. I _____ (learn) about him when my parents and I _____ (visit) Thunder Bay, Ontario. There is a statue there in his honour. I also _____ (see) a movie about his life. This man _____ (have) dignity and great courage. His long fight with cancer _____ (inspire) many other victims of this terrible disease. He _____ (start) the Marathon of Hope. He _____ (want) to run across Canada to raise money for cancer research. In good weather and bad, he _____ (run) along the highways, never stopping in his quest. He _____ (go) from town to town, collecting money to help find a cure for this disease. Unfortunately, he _____ (be, negative) able to complete his marathon. He _____ (die) of cancer before reaching his goal. When I think life is unfair to me, I remember Terry Fox and think my life isn't so bad after all.

WRITTEN PRODUCTION

WRITING ABOUT A PERSONAL HERO

Write about a person who inspires you in a special way. Use about 100 words.

Before writing

Think of a person, living or dead, who inspires you.

Who is this person? _____

How did you find out about this person? _____

What qualities do you associate with this person? _____

What do you know about this person? Note as much information as possible.

_____

_____

What did he or she do to inspire you? _____

_____

What do you think of when you hear this person's name? _____

_____

Your answers to these questions can serve as the outline (plan) of your text.

While writing

Refer to your outline often to make sure your text includes all the points you want to mention. Don't be afraid to modify your outline if you think it is necessary.

Use the following lines to prepare your draft. Use a loose-leaf sheet if you need more space.

_____

_____

_____

_____

_____

_____

_____

_____

After writing

Ask a classmate to read your text. Have that person indicate with a question mark any sentences that seem unclear.

Now, have that person write an outline (plan) of your text.

Did your classmate find it easy or difficult to make the outline?_____

Listen to your classmate's comments and make any necessary adjustments.

Hand in your final version on a loose-leaf sheet.

ORAL PRODUCTION

WHEN I WAS YOUNG...

In teams of four, discuss what you were like when you were a child.

Before discussing

1 List five adjectives that best describe the way you were when you were a child.

Example: *athletic, tall, happy, quiet, studious*

_____   _____   _____

_____   _____

2 Look at the animals on the next page. Write an adjective that describes each animal. Try to use a different adjective for each one.

Sample adjectives: Exotic (kangaroo) Quiet (koala)

3 Get into teams of four. Choose two animals that best suit your personality by comparing the adjectives you used to describe yourself and each animal. Give examples to support your choices.

Example: When I was young, I was like a baby Koala. I was very quiet. You never heard me around the house. I always coloured by myself or read books. I didn't like loud noises so I never made any noise.

While discussing

Listen to what each classmate says and react to each others' descriptions.

- Did anyone on your team choose the same animals as you?
- Did they use the same adjectives to describe that animal and themselves?
- Did anyone use the same adjectives as you, but associated with a different animal?

GRAMMAR

The present continuous tense is used to talk about an action or activity that is in progress at the moment you are speaking. In other words, the activity started some time before you spoke and it will end some time after you finish speaking.

PAST	NOW	FUTURE

You **are reading** this sentence right now.

The present continuous is also used to describe actions that take place over a period of time.

Emily **is learning** how to play the drums.
Jeremy **is working** at the new ski shop.

The present continuous can show that an action will take place in the near future.

Karen **is moving** to Montreal tomorrow.
I**'m seeing** that new action movie with Denis tonight.

AFFIRMATIVE	NEGATIVE	CONTRACTED FORM
Be + main verb + *ing*	*Be* + *not* + main verb + *ing*	
I am reading a magazine now.	I am not reading a magazine now.	I'm (not) reading
You are sitting at your desk.	You are not sitting at your desk.	You're (not) sitting
He/She/It is drinking water.	He/She/It is not drinking water.	He's/She's/It's (not) drinking
We are talking about Jayne.	We are not talking about Jayne.	We're (not) talking
They are travelling in Europe.	They are not travelling in Europe.	They're (not) travelling

Here are some key words that are often used with the present continuous tense:

now • right now • today • this week • this month • this year

 Write the sentences in the present continuous tense.

1. I (to plan) a surprise party for my friend's birthday.

I am/I'm planning a surprise party for my friend's birthday.

2. Everyone (to have) a great time right now.

3. Miranda (to help) Jerry with his homework today.

4. Cybill (to take, negative) her car to school because it's at the garage.

5. He (to fix, negative) my computer.

6. Jack (to shovel) the snow from the driveway now.

7. Mel (to tell) the story of his last home run.

8. I (to give, negative) you my answers.

9. It (to rain, negative) too hard for now.

10. Listen, the baby (to cry).

ASKING QUESTIONS IN THE PRESENT CONTINUOUS TENSE

QW	Aux.	S	V + *ing*	ROQ
	Is	Laura	coming	with us?
	Are	you	listening	to me?
Why	is	she	painting	her car purple?
What	are	they	doing?	

Practice

2 Write the appropriate questions above the answers. Look at the words in bold for clues.

1. Q: _When is Bart brushing his teeth?_

A: Bart is brushing his teeth **right now.**

2. Q: _____

A: Dan and Lucie are **talking on the phone.**

3. Q: _____

A: **Mario** is ordering pizza.

4. Q: _____

A: **No,** Lou isn't cleaning up his room.

5. Q: _____

A: Samantha is baby-sitting **three** children this weekend.

6. Q: _____

A: **Yes,** Meredith and Cynthia are watching a movie.

7. Q: _____

A: Nick and Ron are going **to the Rolling Stones concert** next week.

8. Q: _____

A: **Jamie** is working at the new pet shop.

9. Q: _____

A: **No,** Rick and Matt aren't playing football this year.

10. Q: _____

A: The dog is barking **because it doesn't like the mailman.**

Note that these verbs are **not** normally used in the present continuous tense:

believe • belong • forget • hate • hear • know • like • love • mean • need
prefer • realize • remember • see • seem • suppose • understand • want

---

3 Use the simple present or the present continuous tense to complete the sentences on the next two pages.

Jack and the Peanut Plant

I _____ (take) our cow to the market.

Jack _____ (go) to the market because he _____

_____ (need) money to buy food.

I'm sure you _____ (realize),
you _____ (make) a good deal.

At the market, Jack _____ (believe) a very convincing

merchant _____ (give) him a good deal.

Why _____ (sleep, negative, question), Jack?

Jack _____ (want) to watch the miracle of the peanut plant.

I _____ (believe, negative) it! Look at all these peanut butter jars. It _____ (be) just fabulous. We'll never be hungry again.

The next morning, Jack and his uncle _____ (see) something amazing.

How about a nice glass of milk, Jack?

But, dear Uncle! _____ _____ (remember, negative, question)? I sold our cow yesterday!!!

Jack and his uncle can eat as many peanut butter sandwiches
as they _____ (want).

4 Answer the following questions about the story *Jack and the Peanut Plant.*

1. What fairy tale inspired this story?

_____

2. The original story has been modified in several ways. Name two of them.

_____

_____

3. Stories usually have a beginning, a high point (peak) and an ending. Describe the illustration that corresponds to the high point of the story. Explain your answer.

_____

_____

_____

WRITTEN PRODUCTION

WRITING A CHILDREN'S STORY

Choose from the illustrations on page 116 to make up a story.

Before writing

Brainstorm the vocabulary words you will need for your story.

_____

_____

_____

_____

While writing

Write your draft on a loose-leaf sheet. Follow these guidelines.

GUIDELINES FOR YOUR STORY

• Your story must have a title, a beginning, a peak and an ending.

• Because it is a children's story, your characters should talk.

  Example: *Then, the young girl wakes up and says, "I'm going to the lake to watch the sunrise."*

• Use the simple present and the present continuous forms of the verbs appropriately.

After writing

Once you have written your draft, check to make sure that it respects the guidelines in the *While writing* section.

Pass your final story to a classmate and have them identify the beginning, the peak and the ending of your story. Listen to their comments and make any necessary changes.

Hand in your final version on a loose-leaf sheet.

ORAL PRODUCTION

TELLING STORIES BASED ON PICTURES

For this activity, you'll be in a group of four. Your teacher will give you the illustrations you need.

Before speaking

Each group member chooses a different set of illustrations relating a sequence of events. Look carefully at all the illustrations and help each other with any new vocabulary words.

Look at your own set of pictures and decide what could happen in your story. Think of a title for it.

While speaking

One group member places his or her set of illustrations on the desk. This student starts by telling the title of the story and the setting (where it takes place, who the main characters are, how they are related to each other, etc.). Then, one after another, going around in a clockwise direction, the other students continue the story. The fourth student gives the story an ending, and starts a new story based on his or her own set of cards.

The activity continues until all four stories have been completed.

The Present Continuous

PRODUCTION

LP-4 THE FUTURE

GRAMMAR

The future is used to talk about an action or situation that is yet to occur. There are two ways to form the future: with **will** and with **going to**.

| PAST | NOW | FUTURE ▶ |

▼ ▼

Paul **will** arrive tomorrow.
Paul is **going to** arrive tomorrow.

THE FUTURE WITH **WILL**	
Affirmative *Will* + the main verb	Negative *Will* + *not* + main verb
I will work.	I will not work.
You will work.	You will not work.
He/She/It will work.	He/She/It will not work.
We will work.	We will not work.
They will work.	They will not work.

You can also use the contracted form:

I'll work. I won't work.
He'll work. He won't work.

THE FUTURE WITH **GOING TO**	
Affirmative *Be* + *going to* + main verb	Negative *Be* + *not* + *going to* + main verb
I am going to eat it all.	I'm not going to eat it all.
She is going to eat it all.	She isn't going to eat it all.
They are going to eat it all.	They're not going to eat it all.

Here are some key words that are often used with the future:

next week/month/weekend/Monday/etc. • *soon* • *later* • *tonight* • *tomorrow*
in a few days

Practice

1 Unscramble the sentences to see what these teens are planning to do after high school.

1. visit / a / Mary / Europe / for / will / year

2. CEGEP / and / study / in / Tonya / will / art / Francis

3. semester / next / Paul / won't / school / to / return

4. Tracy / take / course / Bobby / and / will / computer / a

5. will / technical / to / Josianne / school / apply

6. he / take / photography class / Michael / but / won't / in / will a / music / continue

2 Now rewrite the sentences using the **going to** structure.

1.
2.
3.
4.
5.
6.

3 What are you planning to do this weekend? Write three sentences stating what you plan to do and three sentences stating what you won't do this weekend.

Example: *This weekend I'm going to see a movie with my friends. I won't make my bed.*

4 Tell a classmate about your plans. Write down what your classmate tells you.

Example: *This weekend, Michelle is going to see a movie with her friends. She won't make her bed.*

_____

_____

_____

_____

_____

_____

ASKING QUESTIONS ABOUT THE FUTURE

WITH WILL				
QW	*Will*	S	V	ROQ
	Will	you	come	with me?
	Will	they	stay	for supper?
When	will	they	arrive?	

WITH GOING TO					
QW	*To be*	S	*Going to*	V	ROQ
	Are	we	going to	watch	a video?
	Is	Bill	going to	sleep	here tonight?
How	are	you	going to	get	to the arena?

Practice

5 Prepare a questionnaire to find out what your classmates are going to do this summer.

a) Fill in the questionnaire below by writing the appropriate questions. Practise using both forms of the future.

b) Interview your classmates. Follow the examples.

Find someone who... is going to travel to the United States.

Q: *Are you going to travel to the United States this summer?*

A: *Kevin is going to travel to the United States this summer.*

Find someone who... will fly an airplane.

Q: *Will you fly an airplane this summer?*

A: *No one will fly an airplane this summer.*

1. will work in a restaurant.

   Q: _____

   A: _____

2. is going to take summer classes.

   Q: _____

   A: _____

3. is going to sleep all summer.

   Q: _____

   A: _____

4. will visit relatives.

   Q: _____

   A: _____

5. will work with children.

   Q: _____

   A: _____

6 Use the future to complete the following sentences.

After High School

I have great plans for when I finish high school. First, I _____
_____ (spend) the summer at my aunt Theresa's. She lives in Spain.
I _____ (have) the chance to visit my cousin Louis. My aunt
and uncle own a vineyard. I _____ (help) them pick the
grapes they need to make the wine. It _____ (be, negative)
easy. We _____ (have) to work long days. I _____
_____ (stay) with them till September when school starts again.
I think I _____ (benefit) a lot from this experience. This
trip _____ (give) me the opportunity to learn some
Spanish. Next year at CEGEP, I _____ (take) Spanish
classes as well. I _____ (need) to work hard on my Spanish
if I want to become a translator.

GRAMMAR

The Future

PRODUCTION

121

WRITTEN PRODUCTION

AFTER HIGH SCHOOL

Write a short text about what you plan to do after high school. Talk about your plans for the summer and the upcoming year. Use about 100 words.

Complete the following outline by brainstorming all the things you would like to do after high school. Write down details if possible.

Example: *Summer plans: a) Take a trip:* • *go camping with friends*
                                                    • *go to the beach*

Note: You don't have to fill in all the lines.

MY PLANS FOR THE FUTURE

1. Summer plans:

   a) _____

   • _____

   • _____

   b) _____

   • _____

   • _____

   c) _____

   • _____

   • _____

2. Plans for the fall:

   a) _____

   • _____

   • _____

   b) _____

   • _____

   • _____

   c) _____

   • _____

   • _____

3. Plans for the winter:

a) _____

• _____

• _____

b) _____

• _____

• _____

c) _____

• _____

• _____

While writing

To write your text, choose the activities from your outline that you are most likely to do in the next year. Use the following lines to write your draft.

_____

_____

_____

_____

_____

_____

_____

_____

_____

_____

_____

_____

After writing

Exchange books with a classmate and read each other's drafts. Point out the strengths and indicate elements that need to be worked on. Be specific.

Examples:
- *The text is/isn't well structured.*
- *It is/isn't clear and easy to read.*
- *Here are some spelling/grammar errors that need to be corrected.*

Hand in your final version on a loose-leaf sheet.

ORAL PRODUCTION

GOING BACK TO THE FUTURE

In teams of three or four, discuss what your life will be like ten years from now.

Before discussing

Before going into teams, think about the following questions.

- Will you be out of school or still studying?
- Will you be working? What will your job be?
- Will you be married?
- Will you have children?
- Where will you live? (Which country/province/city/etc.?)
- What will your home look like?
- What will you do for pastimes or hobbies?
- Will you have the same friends?

While discussing

After each person speaks, discuss whether his or her vision of the future is realistic or not. Explain your point of view.

GRAMMAR

Modals are used to talk about ability (**can**), possibility (**can, could, may, might**), necessity or obligation (**must**), or permission (**may, can**).

They are also used to give advice (**should**) and to make requests (**can, could, would**).

The expression **have to** is similar to a modal, and in the affirmative, has the same meaning as **must**.

Ability	My dog *can* catch a Frisbee in his mouth.
Possibility	She *could* win a gold medal.
	My hamster Buddy died last week so we *may* get a new one.
	It looks like it *might* snow tonight.
Necessity/Obligation	In England, you *must* drive on the left side of the road.
	You *have to* change the cat's litter box more often.
Permission	*May* I go to my locker?
	You *may* go to your locker, but don't take too much time.
	Can Tiny come out and play?
	You *can* use your markers instead of your pencils.
Advice	Lori *should* make her bed before going to school.
	You *shouldn't* read without your glasses.
Requests	*Can* you take this letter to the post office?
	Could you turn the TV down? I can't hear myself think.
	Would you pass the salt, please?
	I *would* like a peanut butter and banana sandwich, please.

AFFIRMATIVE	NEGATIVE
Modal + base form of verb	Modal + *not* + base form of verb
I can speak many languages.	I can't speak many languages.
You should run faster.	You shouldn't run so fast.
We must drink water to survive.	We mustn't drink so much coffee.

Note that the negative forms of **must** and **have to** have different meanings:

You **must not** drive on the left side in Canada. ▶ You **are obligated** to drive on the right.

You **don't have to** finish this today. ▶ You **are not obligated** to finish it today. You can do it tomorrow.

1. Place each of the following actions under an appropriate heading. Using a modal associated with that heading, complete the sentence. Be prepared to explain your choices. Follow the example.

snow	wash every day	smoke in the hospital
cheat	eat only chocolate	listen to the teacher
sing well	swim twenty laps	eat three meals a day
finish early		study hard if you want to succeed

ABILITY

_____

_____

_____

_____

_____

OBLIGATION

You mustn't smoke in the hospital

because it's a rule.

_____

_____

_____

_____

POSSIBILITY

_____

_____

_____

_____

_____

ADVICE

_____

_____

_____

_____

_____

Underline the appropriate modal from each pair to complete the following text.

A Letter of Opinion:
How Can a Student Succeed at School?

In my opinion, every student (can/would) have the key to success. The first thing you (may/must) do to succeed is to apply yourself. You (should/shouldn't) pay attention in class. If you don't, you (might not/ must not) get the necessary information you need. Of course, you (would/should) study hard and do all your homework; and you (can't/don't have to) give up your social life either. Take the time to relax or you (might/might not) be able to concentrate all the time. And finally, if you have a problem with your subjects, you (can/mustn't) always ask your teachers or a friend for help. If you really want to succeed, you (should/shouldn't) follow my advice.

ASKING QUESTIONS WITH MODALS

QW	Modal	S	Base Form of Verb	ROQ
	Can	he	swim	well?
When	should	I	call?	
	May	we	come	in?

 Unscramble the yes/no questions and the information questions below to complete the chart. Indicate next to each number whether the question suggests a request (R), an obligation (O), an ability (A), permission (P) or advice (AD).

QUESTIONS

1. do / Marty / can / back flip / a / ?
2. I / should / what / in CEGEP / study / ?
3. places / we / change / may / ?
4. my / in / sink / the / could / wash / frog / I / pet / ?
5. leave / bed / must / why / under / your / socks / you / the / dirty / ?
6. backwards / you / the / recite / can / alphabet / ?

		QW	Modal	Subject	Verb	ROQ
(A)	1.		Can	Marty	do	a back flip?
(___)	2.					
(___)	3.					
(___)	4.					
(___)	5.					
(___)	6.					

WRITTEN PRODUCTION

RESTRICTING DRIVER'S LICENSES TO PEOPLE WHO ARE 18 OR OLDER

Write a letter of opinion stating your position on whether or not obtaining a driver's license should be restricted to people 18 years and over. Give at least two arguments to support your position. Use about 100 words.

Before writing

Use a mapping technique to generate your ideas.

1. Take a loose-leaf sheet. Write your position on the topic in the centre of the page.
2. Write ideas related to your position around the centre circle.
3. Draw lines linking the ideas to the circle with your position.
4. Add details around the ideas and link them together.
5. Continue mapping until you have no more ideas.

Example:

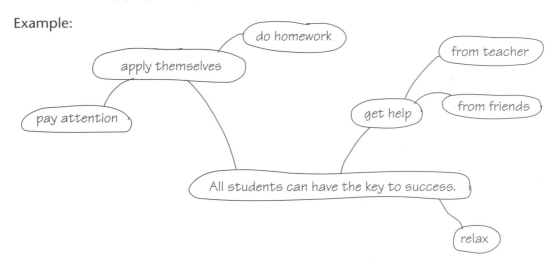

While writing

Use your map as an outline. You don't have to use all the ideas you came up with in your text.

Use the following lines to write your draft.

_____

_____

_____

_____

_____

_____

_____

_____

_____

_____

_____

_____

_____

_____

_____

_____

_____

_____

After writing

Ask a classmate to read your text and to make a map summarizing it.

Look at the map your classmate drew up. Does it show the ideas you are trying to express? Make the necessary corrections and adjustments.

Hand in your final version on a loose-leaf sheet.

ORAL PRODUCTION

WHAT MAKES A GOOD FRIEND?

In groups of four, discuss what makes a good friend.

Before discussing

Answer the following questions on your own.

1. What kind of person are you attracted to?

Example: *A person who is encouraging and friendly.*

_____

_____

_____

2. What kind of person do you try to avoid?

Example: *A person who repeats everything to others.*

_____

_____

_____

3. Think of your closest friends. Why do you like these people?

_____

_____

_____

While discussing

Mention some of the things a good friend should/shouldn't, must/mustn't, can/can't do or say.

Listen to what your classmates say.

Do you agree with their vision of an ideal friend? Express your opinion.

After discussing

As a team, make up a chart representing the ideal friend.

GRAMMAR

The present perfect tense is used to talk about an action or activity that was completed at some time in the past but is still relevant in the present. The time of completion is not mentioned, either because it is not known or because it is not important in the speaker's mind.

| TIME UNKNOWN | NOW | FUTURE |

► ► ►

I **have lost** my keys.
You **have stopped** smoking.

The action or activity may have happened one or more times in the past.

He **has washed** his car at least four times this week.
We **have won** all the games this season.

The *when* is not important. What is important is that the activity or the action was (or was not) *completed* at a certain time in the past.

I **have** never **been** to Disney World but I **have been** to La Ronde.
My friends **have tried** the "911" chicken wings.
Jim **has not done** this magic trick yet.

The present perfect is used to talk about a past action that has consequences in the present.

Mélanie **has** already **left** her apartment. (Consequence: She isn't there now.)
Since 1995, our school **has offered** drama courses. (Consequence: You can take a drama course this year.)

> *Here are some key words that are often used with the present perfect tense:*
>
> *ever • never • yet • already • just • for • recently • lately • so far • since • often*
>
> *Notice their positions in the sentences below.*

Have you **ever eaten** fried worms? No, I **have never eaten** fried worms.
Have the players **finished** the game **yet**? No, they **haven't**.
Has he **already bought** her a present? Yes, he **has just paid** for it.
Have you **read** any good books **lately**? I **haven't read** a good book **since** last month.

USING THE PRESENT PERFECT TENSE

AFFIRMATIVE	NEGATIVE	CONTRACTED FORM
Have/has + past participle of verb (PP)	*Have/has* + *not* + PP	
I have mailed the letter.	I have not mailed the letter.	I've mailed I haven't mailed
You have already seen this show.	You have not seen this show yet.	You've seen You haven't seen
She has read many books.	She has not read many books.	She's read She hasn't read
He has had the chicken pox.	He has not had the chicken pox.	He's had He hasn't had
It has started to rain.	It has not started to rain.	It's started It hasn't started
We have gone to that store.	We have not gone to that store.	We've gone We haven't gone
They have been to P.E.I.	They have not been to P.E.I.	They've been They haven't been

> **Note:**
> *The past participles of regular verbs have the same form as their simple past tense. The past participles of irregular verbs vary and must be memorized. (See page 153 for a list of irregular verbs and their past participles.)*

Practice

Use the groups of words below to form sentences. Make sure to put the verbs in the present perfect tense.

1. with his friends / go / to the basketball game / Phil

_____

2. she / to Mexico / be / never

_____

3. for twenty-five years / live / in the same apartment / they

_____

4. he / on that corner / since eight o'clock / be

_____

5. Jessica and Joan / yet / see / I

(NEGATIVE)

_____

6. finish / her two-hour nap / just / my baby sister

_____

7. our teacher / the date / of the next exam / mention / yet

(NEGATIVE)

_____

8. any problems / we / so far / have

(NEGATIVE)

9. stare / at that cute guy / we / often

_____

_____

10. my favourite hockey team / this season / a single game / win

(NEGATIVE)

_____

_____

ASKING QUESTIONS IN THE PRESENT PERFECT TENSE

QW	Aux.	S	PP	ROQ
What	have	they	done	in English class?
	Have	you	been	there before?
	Has	Greta	found	a date for the dance yet?

Practice

2 Choose five of the sentences from the previous activity and write them in the question form. Write three yes/no questions and two information questions.

_____

_____

_____

_____

_____

_____

_____

_____

_____

3 Scan through the text. Underline the correct form of the verbs in the parentheses.

Emily wants to apply for a summer job at Camp Green Leaf. Here is the cover letter she sent with her résumé (curriculum vitae).

Refer to the explanations for the simple past and the present perfect if you have difficulty.

February 16, _____

Ms. Sophie DeVille
1246 Tour du Lac
Lac Beauport, Qc
H1H 5X9

Dear Ms. De Ville,

Last week, I (saw / have seen) in the local newspaper that you will be needing camp counsellors for next summer.

As you can see in my résumé, I (went / have gone) to one of your camps in 1993 when I (was / have been) 12 years old. So far, I (took / have taken) two camp counsellor courses, as well as drama and juggling classes. Since last year I (gave / have given) art classes at the Musée de La Civilisation. For the last month, I (helped / have helped) three elementary school students do their homework after school.

Last winter I (was / have been) a ski instructor and I (was / have been) responsible for children from 6 to 10 years old. I (loved / have loved) this experience and I think the kids also (liked / have liked) the lessons I (gave / have given) them.

As you can see, I have a lot of experience with children and I would really like to be part of your team next summer.

Yours truly,

Emily Miller

Emily Miller

WRITTEN PRODUCTION

WRITING A COVER LETTER FOR A JOB APPLICATION

When you apply for a job, you have to fill out a job application form and/or send your résumé (curriculum vitae). One way to make a good impression on your future employer is to write a cover letter that gives more details about who you are.

Before writing

Think about the type of job you are applying for.

- Why would you like to have this job?
- What makes you a good candidate for this kind of job?
- Do you have any experience doing a job similar to this one?

You may want to refer to the charts on the present perfect before you start.

While writing

Write about the qualifications, training or skills that could help you do this job, but keep it short. Your job application form or résumé contains all the other information your employer might need. Don't forget to sign your letter!

(DATE)

(ADDRESSEE, IF YOU HAVE THIS INFORMATION)

(ADDRESS)

(CITY/PROVINCE)

(POSTAL CODE)

Dear Mr./Mrs./Ms. _____ ,

_____

_____

_____

_____

_____

_____

_____

_____

Yours truly,

(YOUR SIGNATURE)

After writing

Reread your draft and check your grammar. Use a dictionary to check the spelling of any words you're not sure of.

Remember that your cover letter is a reflection of who you are. If you want to make a good first impression, your letter has to be perfect!

Hand in the final version of your cover letter on a loose-leaf sheet.

ORAL PRODUCTION

JOB INTERVIEWS

In this activity, you'll be playing two roles: an employer who wants to fill a job and a candidate who wants to get one. Your teacher will tell you which role you'll be playing first and when to change roles.

Before the interviews

Read the list of jobs and occupations.

JOBS AND OCCUPATIONS			
Referee	Doctor	Musician	Computer programmer
Sales clerk	Model	Artist	Interior decorator
Travel agent	Teacher	Singer	Interpreter/Translator
Taxi/Bus driver	Mechanic	Chef	Veterinarian
Journalist	Chemist	Writer	Sports instructor
Astronomer	Architect	Hair stylist	Bank teller
Photographer	Spy	Actor	Professional athlete

When you're the job candidate: Write at least three sentences demonstrating why you are a good candidate for a job.

Examples:
- I have designed my own web page.
- I have written many short stories for the school newspaper.
- I have read every magazine on the market about cars and mechanics.

- _____

- _____

- _____

When you're the employer: Choose an occupation. Write three appropriate questions to ask the applicants for this job.

Example: I want to hire ___a model.___

- Have you ever been photographed by a professional photographer?
- Have you ever left your home for a long period of time?
- Have you had any experience as a model?

I want to hire _____

- _____
  _____ ?

- _____
  _____ ?

- _____
  _____ ?

During the interviews

When you're the job candidate, keep track of the most interesting potential employers.

NAMES OF POTENTIAL EMPLOYERS:

_____

_____

_____

_____

_____

_____

When you're the employer, make a list of the candidates who seem most qualified for the job.

NAMES OF INTERESTING JOB CANDIDATES:

_____

_____

_____

_____

_____

GRAMMAR

To show that an object belongs to or with someone, add **'s** after the noun that possesses the object.

> The snowboard belongs to Jeff. It is Jeff**'s** snowboard.
> These skis belong to that lady. They are that lady**'s** skis.

The **'s** is also used to show a relationship between people.

> This is Tanya**'s** father.

For plural nouns that end in **s**, add an apostrophe (**'**), but no **s**.

> The teachers**'** parking space.   Our friends**'** parents.

For proper names that end in **s**, you can add an apostrophe (**'**) or **'s**.

> Charles**'** baby sister.   **or**   Charles**'s** baby sister.

1 Rewrite each of these sentences using the possessive form of the word in bold.

1. This house belongs to my **uncle**.

> This is my uncle's house.

2. The name of their **daughter** is Julie.

_____

3. The jeans of my **brother** are black.

_____

4. The new girlfriend of **James** is a figure skater.

_____

5. The soccer team for **women** won their last game.

_____

6. Mrs. Griffiths is in the lounge for the **teachers**.

_____

7. The boss of **Harriet** put her in charge of the department.

_____

8. He spilled his root beer on the beautiful graduation dress of my **sister**.

_____

THE POSSESSIVE FORMS

PERSONAL PRONOUNS	OBJECT PRONOUNS	POSSESSIVE ADJECTIVES	POSSESSIVE PRONOUNS
I have a dog.	The dog belongs to **me**.	It is **my** dog.	The dog is **mine**.
You own a car.	The car belongs to **you**.	It is **your** car.	The car is **yours**.
He bought a new sweater.	The sweater belongs to **him**.	It is **his** sweater.	The sweater is **his**.
She received a letter.	The letter belongs to **her**.	It is **her** letter.	The letter is **hers**.
The cat has a toy mouse.	The toy mouse belongs to **it**.	It is **its** toy mouse.	——————
We have a new house.	The house belongs to **us**.	It is **our** house.	The house is **ours**.
They received an award.	The award belongs to **them**.	It is **their** award.	The award is **theirs**.

P r a c t i c e

2 Complete numbers 2 to 4 in the chart by using the information provided. Then, do 2 sentences of your own.

THE POSSESSIVE FORMS

	OBJECT PRONOUNS	POSSESSIVE ADJECTIVES	POSSESSIVE PRONOUNS
1.	This goldfish belongs to me.	It is my goldfish.	It is mine.
2.	The computer belongs to you.		
3.		It is his birthday gift.	
4.			The red car is hers.
5.			
6.			

3 Read the sentences below and circle the correct form of the words.

Working and Motherhood

1. We all know the old saying, "A woman (s' / 's) place is in the home."
   Well I would like to express my opinion on working mothers.

2. First, let me say that I believe in the advantages working mothers bring to
   society and to (their / them / theirs) families.

3. For example, one of my neighbours (' / 's) son went into day-care when he
   was just a baby in diapers, and I have the impression that no other child I
   know is more mature and sociable than he is.

4. So I feel that this day-care experience was a definite plus, both for (her /
   hers) and for (her / hers) child.

5. Another thing, it seems that children benefit from (their / them / theirs)
   mother ('s / s') experience when she works outside the home, because they
   get more than the parent (' / 's) view of the world.

6. Finally, I think that working mothers also improve (their / them / theirs)
   families (' / 's) quality of life by bringing home an extra salary.

7. To conclude, let me say that I'm for mothers who work, as long as (their /
   theirs) children are well taken care of.

4 Circle the words above that serve as links between the sentences.
   Example: (Another thing)

5 Underline the words or phrases used to express an opinion.
   Example: have the impression

WRITTEN PRODUCTION

STATING YOUR OPINION

Give your opinion about one of the following topics:

a) Parents know what is best for their children.
b) Teens shouldn't date until they're sixteen years old.
c) Looks are very important to teenagers.
d) Television affects human behaviour.
e) Adults are better drivers than teenagers.

Before writing

Choose one of the topics from the list above.

Make some notes while you do your planning.

• Decide what point of view you want to present and what your arguments will be.
• Think of some examples you can give to support your ideas.
• Think of a good introduction that will make the reader want to continue.
• Think of a conclusion.

While writing

Referring to the notes you made while planning, write an organized draft.

Use at least two of each of the following:

• possessive forms
• linking words
• words or phrases that express an opinion

Refer to the charts on the possessive forms.

The Possessive Forms

After writing

Check your draft for the following:

- Do you have an introduction and a conclusion?
- Does your introduction state your position clearly?
- Are your ideas logically organized?
- Did you give examples to support your opinion?
- Did you use two possessive forms, two linking words and two phrases that express an opinion?

Underline, circle or highlight each of these elements in your text.
Hand in your final version on a loose-leaf sheet.

ORAL PRODUCTION

ONE BIG, HAPPY FAMILY

This activity is modelled on the game Battleship. You and a partner will be asking each other questions to try to figure out how the people in the grid are related to each other.

speaking

Look at the grid below. On your own, fill it in, making choices about how Robin, Jess, Sam, Claude and Danny are related to Alex, Sandy, Jean and Pat.

Example:

	ALEX IS...	SANDY IS...	
Robin's	☒	☐	mother
Jess'	☐	☒	father

Alex is Robin's mother.   Sandy is Jess' father.

Notice that all of the names can be used for either males or females.

When you have finished, join a classmate, but don't show him/her your grid!

	ALEX IS...	SANDY IS...	JEAN IS...	PAT IS...	
1. Robin's	☐	☐	☐	☐	mother
2. Jess'	☐	☐	☐	☐	father
3. Sam's	☐	☐	☐	☐	sister
4. Claude's	☐	☐	☐	☐	brother
5. Danny's	☐	☐	☐	☐	cousin

speaking

Take turns with your partner asking yes/no questions to guess each other's choices.

Example: Is Pat Robin's mother?

If the answer is "yes," you may ask another question. If the answer is "no," it's your partner's turn to ask you a question. Keep track of the right answers in the second grid. When one of you has figured out all of the other's choices, this part of the activity is over.

ORAL PRODUCTION

The Possessive Forms

PRODUCTION

	ALEX IS...	SANDY IS...	JEAN IS...	PAT IS...	
1. Robin's	☐	☐	☐	☐	mother
2. Jess'	☐	☐	☐	☐	father
3. Sam's	☐	☐	☐	☐	sister
4. Claude's	☐	☐	☐	☐	brother
5. Danny's	☐	☐	☐	☐	cousin

After speaking

Write three affirmative sentences, three negative sentences and three questions using the possessive form and the information you discovered about your partner's choices.

Examples: Pat is Claude's brother.   Jean isn't Sam's sister.   Who is Alex's cousin?

AFFIRMATIVE SENTENCES

_____

_____

_____

_____

_____

NEGATIVE SENTENCES

_____

_____

_____

_____

_____

QUESTIONS

_____

_____

_____

_____

_____

_____

The Past Continuous

GRAMMAR

The past continuous is used to indicate that an activity or action was happening during a certain period in the past.

PAST	NOW	FUTURE

Yesterday afternoon I **was snowboarding** with my friends.

It also indicates that an action was in progress when another action took place.

I **was sleeping** when the earthquake hit.
The phone rang while I **was taking** a shower.

Notice the key words **when** and **while**. **When** usually introduces a simple past; **while** introduces a past continuous.

We **were working** on the computers **when** the power **failed**.
Martine **twisted** her ankle **while** she **was jogging**.

AFFIRMATIVE	NEGATIVE
Was/were + main verb + *-ing*	*Was/were* + *not* + main verb + *-ing*
I was jumping.	I was not jumping. (I wasn't jumping.)
You were jumping.	You were not jumping. (You weren't jumping.)
He/She/It was jumping.	He/She/It was not jumping. (He/She/It wasn't jumping.)
We were jumping.	We were not jumping. (We weren't jumping.)
They were jumping.	They were not jumping. (They weren't jumping.)

Practice

 1 Write five sentences using the past continuous tense. Choose from the activities in the box. Give extra information when possible.

Study	Watch TV	Cook supper	Walk to school
Ride the bus	Read a book	Eat lunch	Play a video game
Play sports	Listen to music		

Example: Yesterday at 1:55, I was playing basketball in the gym.

1. _____

   _____

2. _____

   _____

3. _____

4. _____

5. _____

2 Now rewrite those sentences using the negative form.

Example: Yesterday at 1:55, I wasn't playing basketball in the gym.

1. _____

2. _____

3. _____

4. _____

5. _____

3 Match actions from column A with actions from column B to make up five complete sentences that use the simple past and the past continuous tenses. Use **when** or **while** in each sentence.

A	B
jog in the park	see a skunk
swim in the ocean	bed breaks
jump on the bed	trip over a rock
ride a bike	pencil breaks
walk down the road	lose your bathing suit
write an exam	get a flat tire

Example: I was writing an exam when my pencil broke.   **or**
My pencil broke while I was writing an exam.

1. _____
2. _____
3. _____
4. _____
5. _____

4 Complete the following sentences. Use your imagination!

1. _____ they heard a strange noise.

2. We were driving around town when _____

3. _____ Tod was taking his shower.

4. I was drinking a soda when _____

5. The teacher walked into the classroom while _____

ASKING QUESTIONS IN THE PAST CONTINUOUS TENSE

QW	Aux.	S	V + *ing*	ROQ
	Were	you	studying	when Nick phoned?
	Was	it	raining	when you woke up?
What	were	you	singing	when I came in?

Practice

5 Prepare five yes/no questions to ask a classmate about what he or she was doing last Saturday night at eight o'clock.

Example: *Were you watching television last Saturday at eight p.m.?*

Q. _____

Q. _____

Q. _____

Q. _____

Q. _____

Now ask a classmate your questions.
Were you able to discover what he or she was doing? _____

6 Underline the correct form of the verbs to complete the following text.

Jill's Childhood Memory

I clearly remember the year my sister Kathleen and I (spent/were spending) Christmas at our grandparents' house. While we (visited/were visiting), something strange (happened/was happening). It was Christmas Eve and we thought we were alone in the house. We (lay/were lying) on Granny's bed trying to sleep when we (heard/were hearing) sounds coming from downstairs. We (decided/were deciding) to investigate the noise. We (opened/were opening) the bedroom door and (walked/were walking) to the top of the staircase hand in hand. We (crept/were creeping) down the stairs when we (heard/ were hearing) the kitchen door slam shut. We (ran/were running) back up the stairs, (hopped/were hopping) into bed and (pulled/ were pulling) the blankets over our heads. I (shivered/was shivering) with fear, wondering who had made the noise, when my sister (whispered/was whispering) that it must have been Santa Claus. While we (discussed/were discussing) this possibility, Granny (came/was coming) into the house shouting "Merry Christmas."

(continued)

Before she could add "And a Happy New Year," we were down the stairs opening every present we could get our hands on. Thinking back, I realize that we were never alone in the house and that Granny had probably placed the gifts under the tree. But something deep inside of me would rather believe that Santa visited us that night, seven years ago.

WRITTEN PRODUCTION

WRITING ABOUT A CHILDHOOD MEMORY

Write about a happy childhood memory that has touched you in a special way. Use between 125 and 150 words to tell your story.

Before writing

Answer the following questions to help you prepare your story.

1. Who was involved? _____

_____

2. Where did this event take place? _____

_____

3. When did it happen? _____

_____

4. What event or events led up to the main event? _____

_____

5. What happened after? _____

_____

6. How did you feel? _____

_____

7. What makes this event so special to you? _____

_____

While writing

Use the following lines to free-write your draft. This version will be for you only, so don't worry about spelling or grammar mistakes yet. Simply write your story as best you can using the information you listed. If you cannot find the word to say what you mean, rephrase your sentence using synonyms. Remember, there is always more than one way to express your meaning. Use a loose-leaf sheet if you need more space.

_____

_____

_____

_____

_____

_____

_____

_____

_____

_____

_____

After writing

Use the following checklist as you reread your text.

- ☐ Check your spelling. Use the dictionary to look up any words you are unsure of.
- ☐ Check your grammar.
  - ☐ Verify your verb tenses. If one event occurred while another was happening, use the simple past and the past continuous.

    Example: We **were eating** outside when it **started** to rain.
  - ☐ Make sure your verb agrees with the subject.

    Example: I **was** /We **were**
  - ☐ Use the correct plural form of nouns.

    Example: There were twenty **people** and only fifteen **chairs.**
- ☐ Check your word order, for example: a subject, a verb and the rest of the sentence.
- ☐ Make sure your sentences aren't too long.

Make any necessary revisions and hand in your final version on a loose-leaf sheet.

ORAL PRODUCTION

TALKING ABOUT EMBARRASSING SITUATIONS

In groups of three or four, tell your classmates about an embarrassing moment in your life.

Before discussing

Before you go into your group, ask yourself the following questions to help refresh your memory.

1. Who were the people involved in your story? _____

_____

2. When did this story take place? _____

_____

3. Where did it happen?_____

_____

4. Were you doing anything special when this event happened? Explain.

_____

_____

5. Were the other people doing anything special?

_____

_____

6. What was your reaction?

_____

_____

7. How did the other people react?

_____

_____

While discussing

When it's not your turn to talk, listen to the other members of your group. Ask questions to get more information on their story. Tell your classmates how you feel about their stories.

Verbs

VERB *TO BE*			
Affirmative **PRESENT**	Negative	Affirmative **PAST**	Negative
I am/I'm	I am not/I'm not	I was	I was not/I wasn't
You are/you're	You are not/you're not/you aren't	You were	You were not/you weren't
He is/he's	He is not/he's not/he isn't	He was	He was not/he wasn't
She is/she's	She is not/she's not/she isn't	She was	She was not/she wasn't
It is/it's	It is not/it's not/it isn't	It was	It was not/it wasn't
We are/we're	We are not/we're not/we aren't	We were	We were not/we weren't
They are/they're	They are not/they're not/they aren't	They were	They were not/they weren't

OTHER VERBS			
Simple Affirmative	Negative	*Continuous* Affirmative	Negative
PRESENT			
I run	I do not/I don't run	I am running/I'm running	I'm not running
You run	You don't run	You are running/you're running	You're not running
He runs	He doesn't run	He is running/he's running	He isn't running
She runs	She doesn't run	She is running/she's running	She isn't running
It runs	It doesn't run	It is running/it's running	It isn't running
We run	We don't run	We are running/we're running	We aren't running
They run	They don't run	They are running/they're running	They aren't running
PAST			
I ran	I did not/I didn't run	I was running	I wasn't running
You ran	You didn't run	You were running	You weren't running
He/she/it ran	He/she/it didn't run	He/she/it was running	It wasn't running
We ran	We didn't run	We were running	We weren't running
They ran	They didn't run	They were running	They weren't running
FUTURE			
WITH *WILL:*		WITH *GOING TO:*	
I will/I'll run	I will not/I won't run	I'm going to run	I'm not going to run
You will/You'll run	You won't run	You're going to run	You're not going to run
He will/He'll run	He won't run	He's going to run	He's not going to run
She will/She'll run	She won't run	She's going to run	She's not going to run
It will/It'll run	It won't run	It's going to run	It's not going to run
We will/We'll run	We won't run	We're going to run	We're not going to run
They will/They'll run	They won't run	They're going to run	They're not going to run

Questions

VERB *TO BE*			
Yes/no questions		**Information questions**	
PRESENT	PAST	PRESENT	PAST
Am I...?	Was I...?	Why are you...?	Why were you...?
Are you...?	Were you...?	How are you?	How were you?
Is he....?	Was he...?	Who is he?	Who was he?
Is she...?	Was she...?	Where is she?	Where was she?
Is it...?	Was it...?	When is it?	When was it?
Are we...?	Were we...?	How tall are we?	How tall were we?
Are they...?	Were they...?	What are they?	What were they?

OTHER VERBS			
Yes/no questions **Simple**	Information questions	Yes/no questions **Continuous**	Information questions
PRESENT			
Do you run?	How fast do you run?	Are you running?	When are you running?
Does he run?	Why does he run?	Is he running?	Where are you running?
PAST			
Did you run?	When did you run?	Were you running?	When were you running?
Did he run?	Why did he run?	Was he running?	Where was he running?
FUTURE			
WITH *WILL:*		WITH *GOING TO:*	
Will I run?	When will I run?	Are you going to run?	When are you going to run?
Will she run?	Why will she run?	Is it going to run?	How is it going to run?

Modals

Affirmative	Negative	Yes/no questions	Information questions
I may go	I may not go	May I go?	When may I go?
You would like	You wouldn't like	Would you like...?	What would you like?
He can swim	He can't swim	Can he swim?	How well can he swim?
She must leave	She mustn't leave	Must she leave?	Why must she leave?
It might rain	It might not rain	Will it rain?	When will it rain?
We could have	We couldn't have	Could we have?	What could we have?
They should go	They shouldn't go	Should they go?	Where should they go?

Irregular Verbs

VERB	SIMPLE PAST	PAST PARTICIPLE	FRENCH
to arise	arose	arisen	*se lever/surgir*
to awake	awoke	awoken	*s'éveiller*
to be	was, were	been	*être*
to bear	bore	borne/born	*enfanter/porter*
to beat	beat	beat/beaten	*battre*
to become	became	become	*devenir*
to begin	began	begun	*commencer*
to bend	bent	bent	*courber/plier*
to bet	bet	bet	*parier*
to bid	bade/bid	bidden/bid	*ordonner*
to bind	bound	bound	*lier/relier*
to bite	bit	bitten/bit	*mordre*
to bleed	bled	bled	*saigner*
to blow	blew	blown	*souffler/gonfler*
to break	broke	broken	*briser/casser*
to breed	bred	bred	*élever/accoupler*
to bring	brought	brought	*apporter*
to build	built	built	*construire/bâtir*
to burn	burned/burnt	burned/burnt	*brûler*
to burst	burst	burst	*éclater*
to buy	bought	bought	*acheter*
to cast	cast	cast	*jeter/mouler*
to catch	caught	caught	*attraper*
to choose	chose	chosen	*choisir*
to cling	clung	clung	*s'accrocher/coller*
to come	came	come	*venir*
to cost	cost	cost	*coûter*
to creep	crept	crept	*ramper*
to cut	cut	cut	*couper*
to deal	dealt	dealt	*distribuer*
to dig	dug	dug	*creuser*
to dive	dove/dived	dived	*plonger*
to do	did	done	*faire/accomplir*
to draw	drew	drawn	*tirer/dessiner*
to dream	dreamed/dreamt	dreamed/dreamt	*rêver*
to drink	drank	drunk	*boire*
to drive	drove	driven	*conduire*
to dwell	dwelled/dwelt	dwelled/dwelt	*demeurer/habiter*
to eat	ate	eaten	*manger*
to fall	fell	fallen	*tomber*
to feed	fed	fed	*nourrir*
to feel	felt	felt	*(se) sentir*
to fight	fought	fought	*combattre/lutter*

Verb	Simple Past	Past Participle	French
to find	found	found	*trouver*
to flee	fled	fled	*fuir*
to fling	flung	flung	*lancer/jeter*
to fly	flew	flown	*voler/s'envoler*
to forbid	forbade	forbidden	*défendre/ interdire*
to forget	forgot	forgotten	*oublier*
to forgive	forgave	forgiven	*pardonner*
to freeze	froze	frozen	*geler*
to get	got	gotten/got	*obtenir/devenir*
to give	gave	given	*donner*
to go	went	gone	*aller*
to grind	ground	ground	*moudre*
to grow	grew	grown	*croître/grandir*
to hang	hung	hung	*suspendre*
to have	had	had	*avoir*
to hear	heard	heard	*entendre*
to hide	hid	hidden	*cacher*
to hit	hit	hit	*heurter/frapper*
to hold	held	held	*tenir*
to hurt	hurt	hurt	*blesser*
to keep	kept	kept	*garder*
to kneel	knelt	knelt	*s'agenouiller*
to knit	knit	knit	*tricoter*
to know	knew	known	*connaître/savoir*
to lay	laid	laid	*poser/placer*
to lead	led	led	*mener/conduire*
to leap	leaped/leapt	leaped/leapt	*bondir/sauter*
to learn	learned/learnt	learned/learnt	*apprendre*
to leave	left	left	*laisser/partir*
to lend	lent	lent	*prêter*
to let	let	let	*laisser/permettre*
to lie	lay	lain	*s'étendre*
to light	lit/lighted	lit/lighted	*allumer*
to lose	lost	lost	*perdre*
to make	made	made	*faire/fabriquer*
to mean	meant	meant	*signifier*
to meet	met	met	*rencontrer*
to mistake	mistook	mistaken	*se tromper*
to mow	mowed	mown/mowed	*tondre*
to pay	paid	paid	*payer*
to put	put	put	*mettre*
to read	read	read	*lire*
to rid	rid	rid	*débarasser*

Verb	Simple Past	Past Participle	French
to ride	rode	ridden	*monter (cheval)*
to ring	rang	rung	*sonner*
to rise	rose	risen	*se lever/monter*
to run	ran	run	*courir*
to saw	sawed	sawed/sawn	*scier*
to say	said	said	*dire/déclarer*
to see	saw	seen	*voir*
to seek	sought	sought	*chercher*
to sell	sold	sold	*vendre*
to send	sent	sent	*envoyer*
to set	set	set	*placer/régler*
to sew	sewed	sewn/sewed	*coudre*
to shake	shook	shaken	*secouer/agiter*
to shed	shed	shed	*verser/répandre*
to shine	shone	shone	*briller/polir*
to shoot	shot	shot	*tirer*
to show	showed	shown	*montrer*
to shrink	shrank	shrunk	*rétrécir/refouler*
to shut	shut	shut	*fermer*
to sing	sang	sung	*chanter*
to sink	sank	sunk	*enfoncer/couler*
to sit	sat	sat	*(s')asseoir*
to slay	slew	slain	*tuer*
to sleep	slept	slept	*dormir*
to slide	slid	slid	*glisser*
to slit	slit	slit	*fendre/séparer*
to smell	smelled/smelt	smelled/smelt	*sentir/humer*
to sow	sowed	sown	*semer*
to speak	spoke	spoken	*parler*
to speed	sped	sped	*hâter*
to spell	spelled/spelt	spelled/spelt	*épeler*
to spend	spent	spent	*dépenser*
to spill	spilled/spilt	spilled/spilt	*renverser*
to spin	spun	spun	*filer/tourner*
to spit	spat/spit	spit	*cracher*
to split	split	split	*fendre/diviser*
to spoil	spoiled/spoilt	spoiled/spoilt	*gâter/gâcher*
to spread	spread	spread	*étendre/ répandre*
to spring	sprang	sprung	*s'élancer*
to stand	stood	stood	*être debout*
to steal	stole	stolen	*voler/dérober*
to stick	stuck	stuck	*coller*
to stink	stank	stunk	*puer*

Verb	Simple Past	Past Participle	French
to strike	struck	struck/stricken	frapper
to string	strung	strung	enfiler/ficeler
to swear	swore	sworn	jurer
to sweat	sweat	sweat	suer/transpirer
to sweep	swept	swept	balayer
to swell	swelled	swollen	enfler/gonfler
to swim	swam	swum	nager
to swing	swung	swung	balancer/osciller
to take	took	taken	prendre
to teach	taught	taught	enseigner
to tear	tore	torn	déchirer
to tell	told	told	dire/raconter
to think	thought	thought	penser
to throw	threw	thrown	lancer/envoyer
to tread	trod	trod/trodden	marcher
to understand	understood	understood	comprendre
to undo	undid	undone	défaire
to upset	upset	upset	bouleverser
to wake	woke	woken/woke	(se) réveiller
to wear	wore	worn	porter
to weave	wove	woven	tisser
to weep	wept	wept	pleurer
to win	won	won	gagner
to wind	wound	wound	enrouler/ remonter
to withdraw	withdrew	withdrawn	(se) retirer
to withstand	withstood	withstood	tolérer/supporter
to wring	wrung	wrung	tordre
to write	wrote	written	écrire